Bar code

BEACH BOYS

Wise Publications
London/New York/Sydney

Exclusive distributors:
Music Sales Limited
8/9 Frith Street,
London W1V 5TZ,
England.
Music Sales Pty Limited
120 Rothschild Avenue,
Rosebery, NSW 2018,
Australia.

Order No. AM77579
ISBN 0.7119.2080.X

Book design by Pearce Marchbank Studio
Cover photograph by Robert Harding Library
Music compiled by Peter Evans

Printed in the United Kingdom by
Caligraving Limited, Thetford, Norfolk.

GOOD VIBRATIONS

Words & Music by Brian Wilson & Mike Love

C
Bb
gen - tle word,
in her eyes,
On_ the wind that lifts her
She_ goes with me to a
A
C7
per - fume through the air.
blos - som world.
CHORUS
F
Cm7
I'm pick-ing up GOOD VI-BRA-TIONS, She's giv-ing me ex-ci-ta-tions.
I'm pick-ing up GOOD VI-BRA-TIONS, She's giv-ing me ex-ci-ta-tions.

G
Dm7
G
Dm7
G
Dm7
G
Dm7
I'm pick-ing up GOOD VI-BRA-TIONS, She's giv-ing me ex-ci-ta-tions.

A
Em7
A
Em7
1
A
Em7
A
Em7
I'm pick-ing up GOOD VI-BRA-TIONS, She's giv-ing me ex-ci-ta-tions.

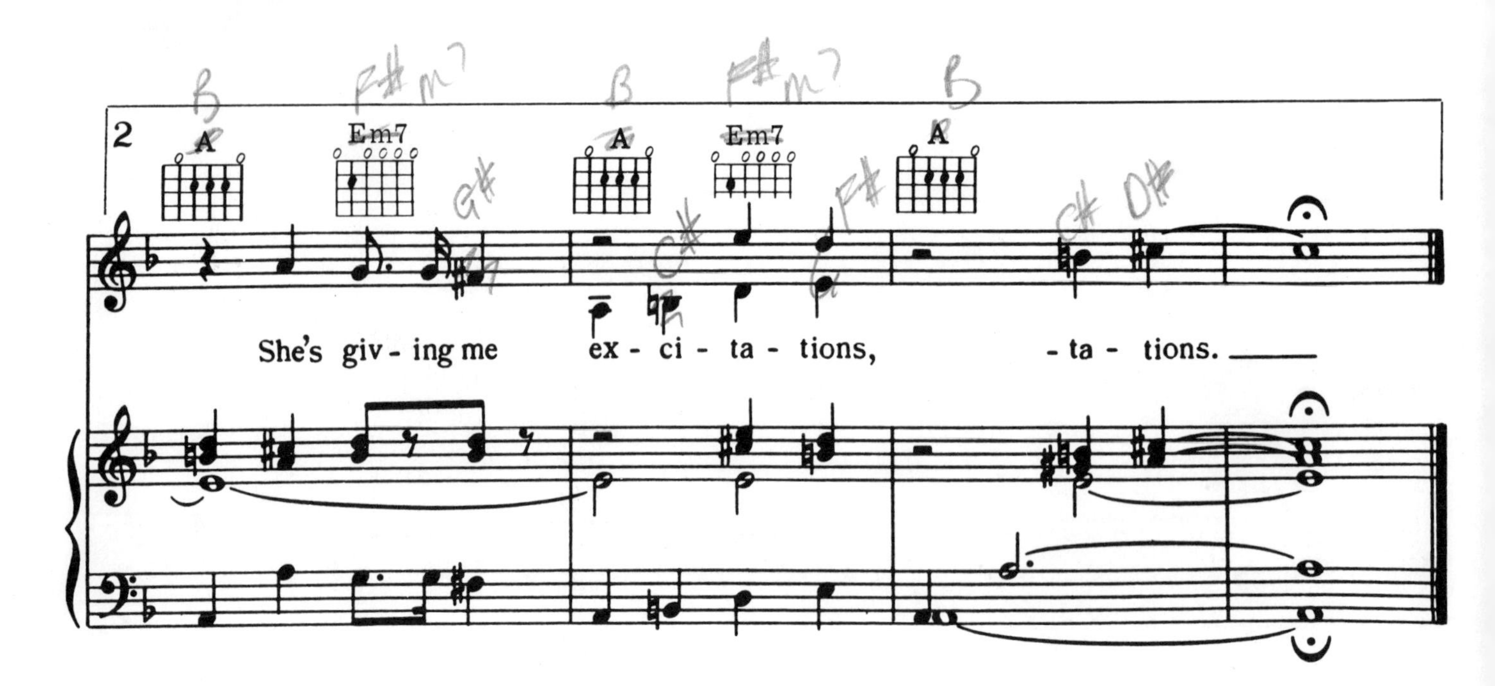
2
A
Em7
A
Em7
A
She's giv-ing me ex-ci-ta-tions, -ta-tions.

SLOOP JOHN B

Words & Music by Brian Wilson

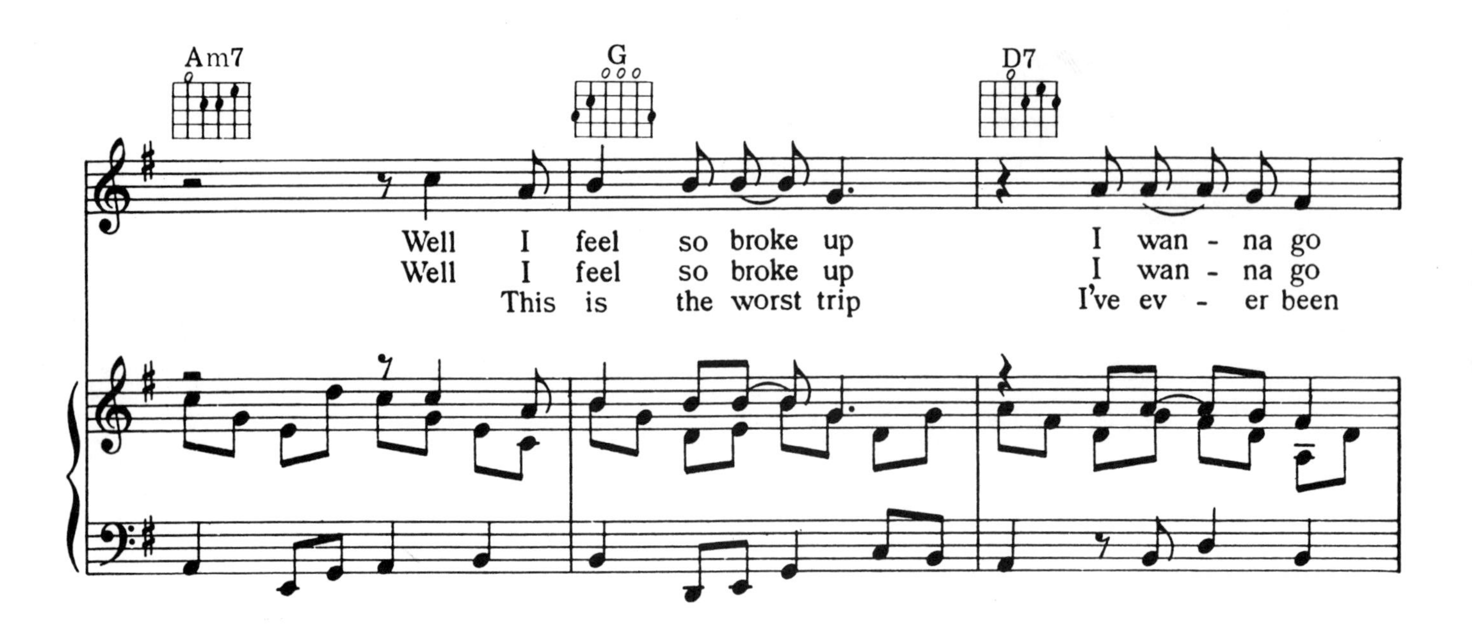
Am7
G
D7
Well I feel so broke up I wan - na go
Well I feel so broke up I wan - na go
This is the worst trip I've ev - er been

G
2
G
home
home
on
So hoist up the John B sail

See how the main sail set
Call for the Cap-tain a - shore
Let me go

D
G
home
Let_ me go
home
I wan - na go

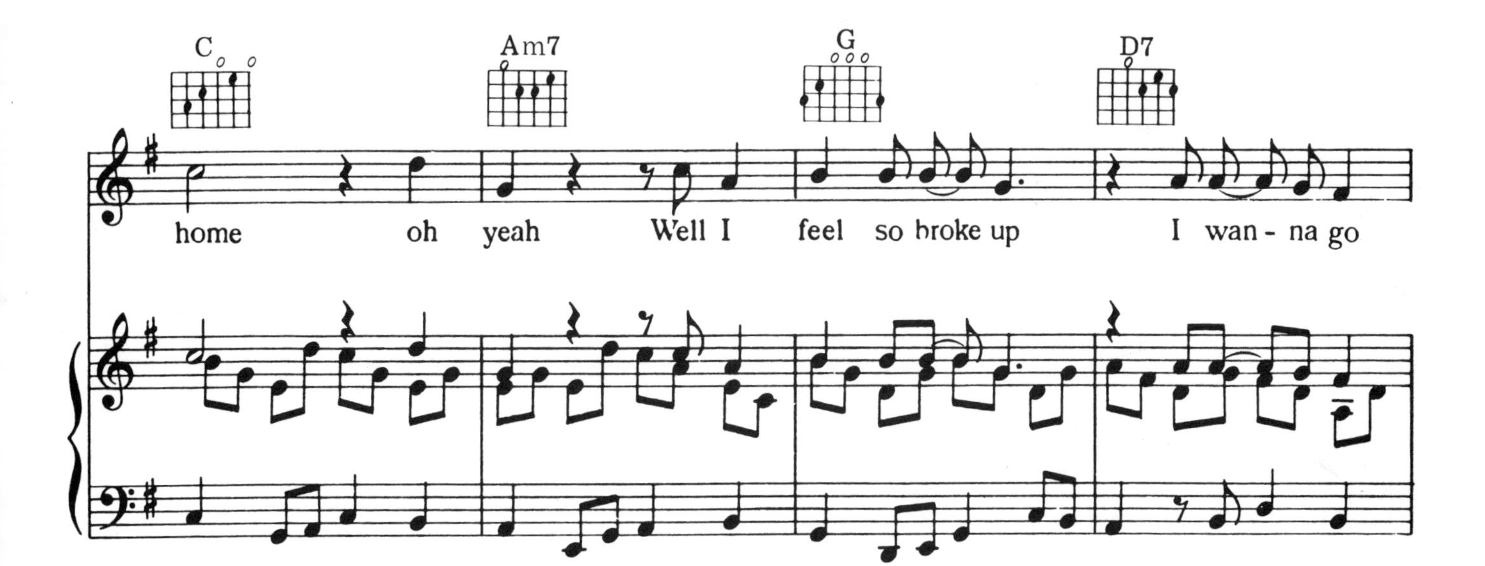
C
Am7
G
D7
home
oh
yeah
Well I
feel
so broke up
I wan - na go

1 & 2
G
3
G
home.
So
home.

ALL SUMMER LONG

Words & Music by Brian Wilson

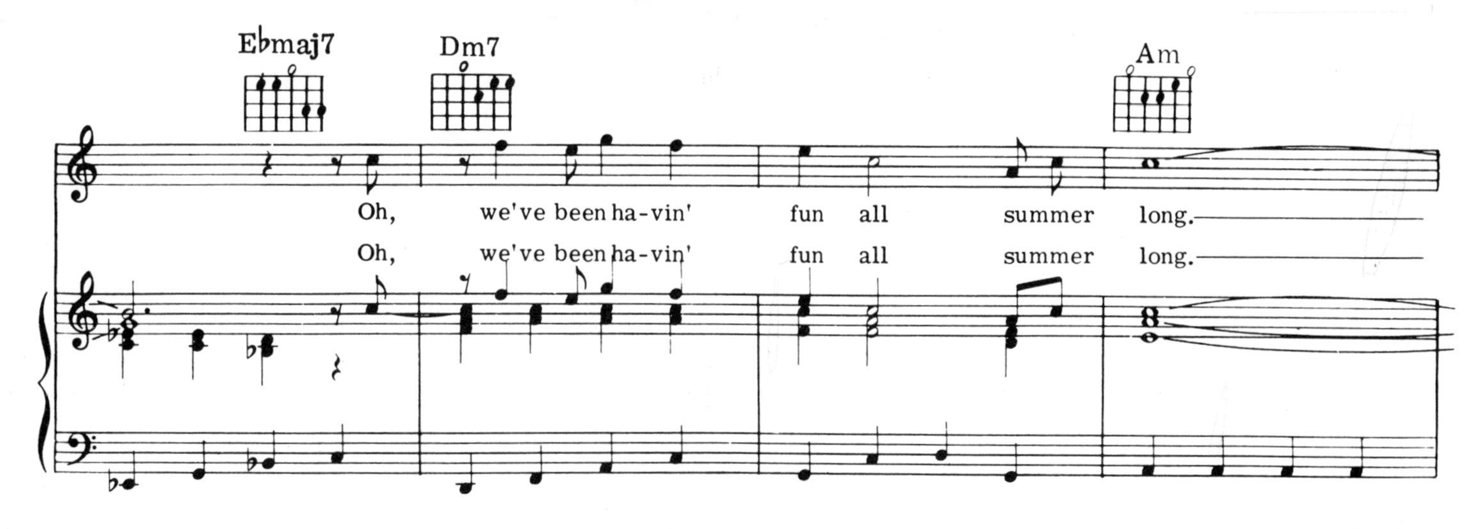

E♭maj7
Dm7
Am
Oh, we've been ha-vin' fun all summer long.
Oh, we've been ha-vin' fun all summer long.

C
F
C
F6
fine.
All sum - mer long you've been with me, I can't see enough of you;

C7
F
D7
Am7
All sum - mer long we've both been free, Won't be long till

D7
D7+
G7
G7+
sum - mer - time is through.
Ad lib.
(But not for us now)
Da Capo
Al Fine

DISNEY GIRLS (1957)

Words & Music by Bruce Johnston

Moderato

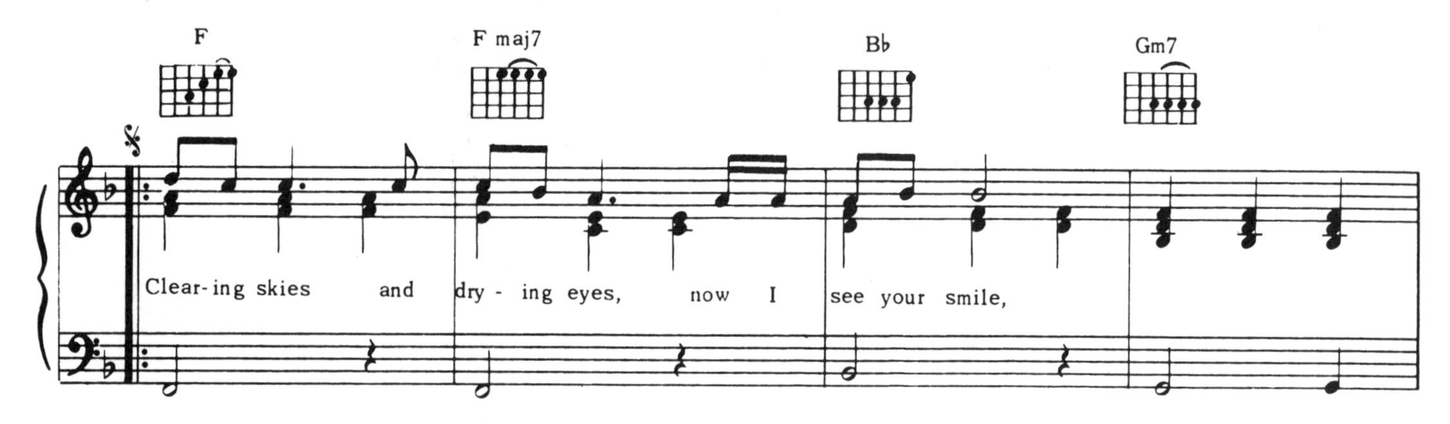

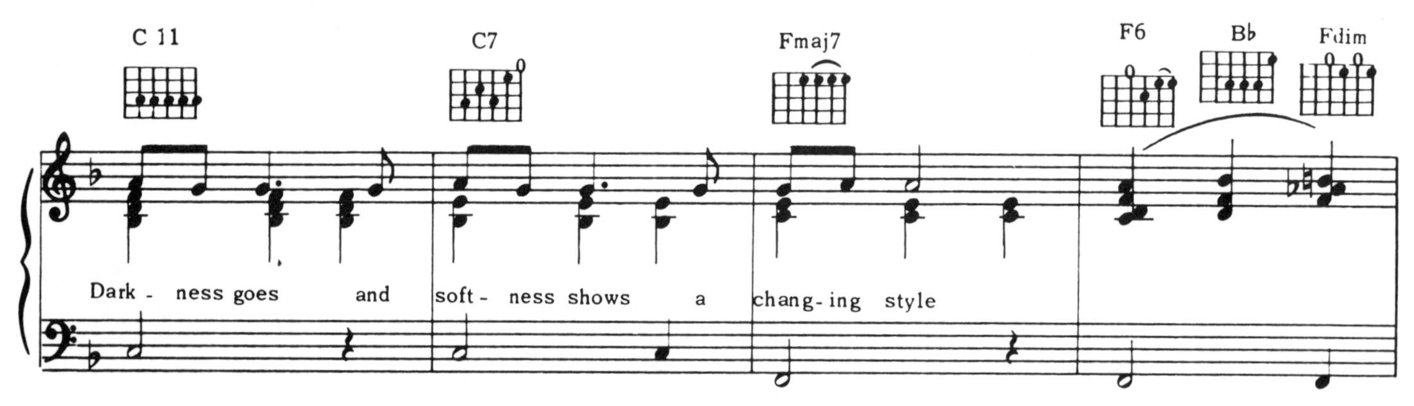

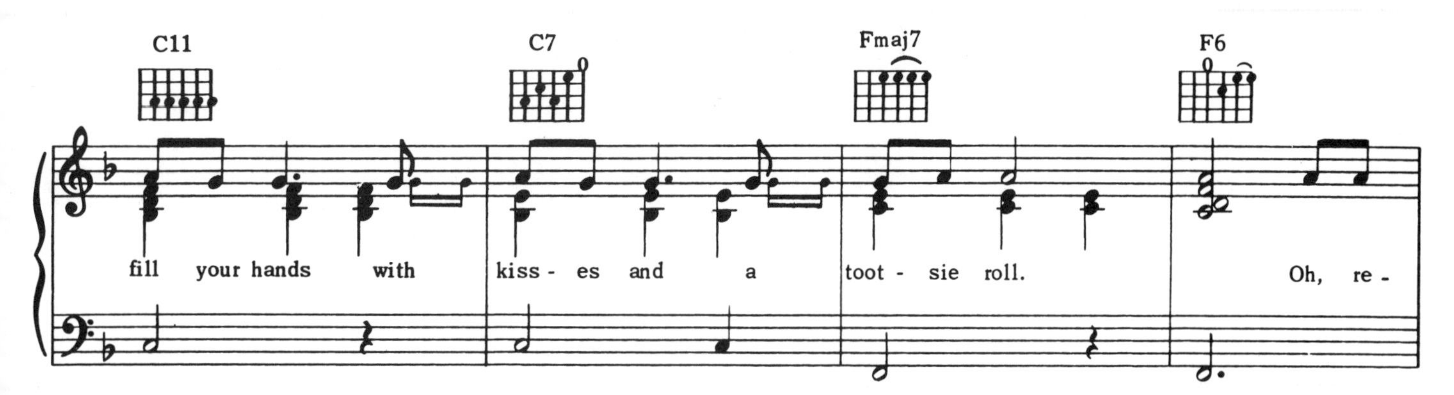
C11
C7
Fmaj7
F6
fill your hands with kiss - es and a toot - sie roll. Oh, re -

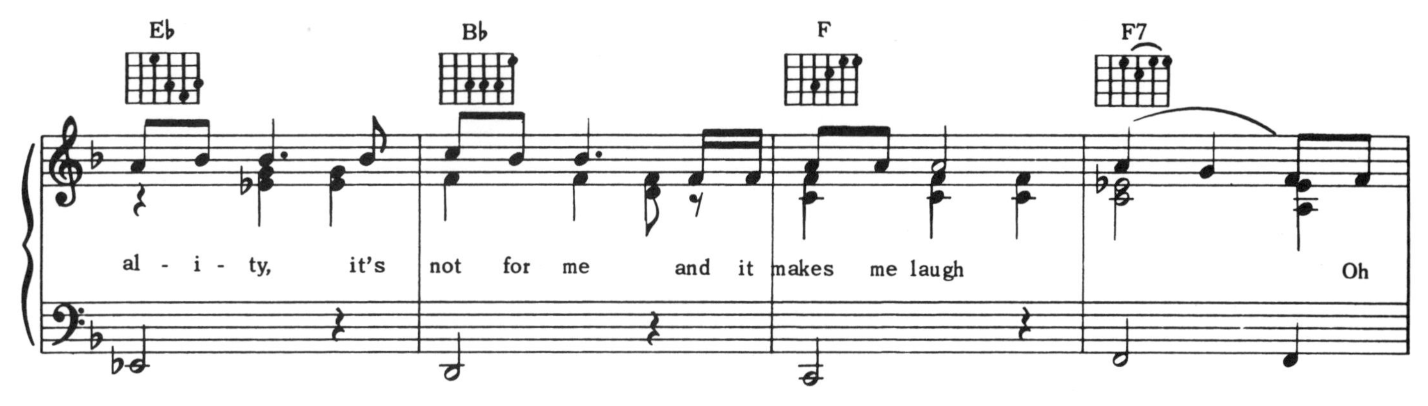
Eb
Bb
F
F7
al - i - ty, it's not for me and it makes me laugh Oh

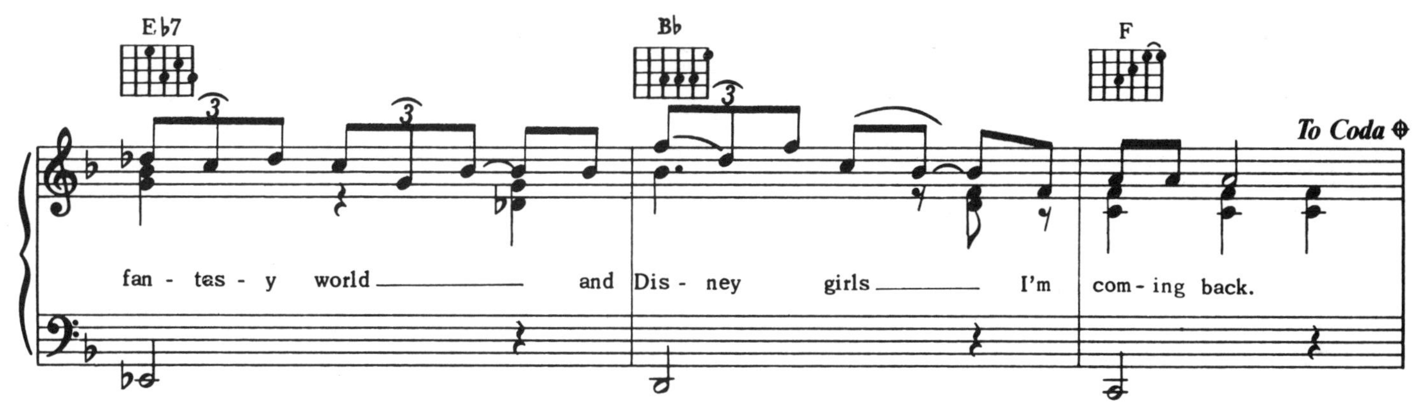
Eb7
Bb
F
To Coda
fan - tas - y world and Dis - ney girls I'm com - ing back.

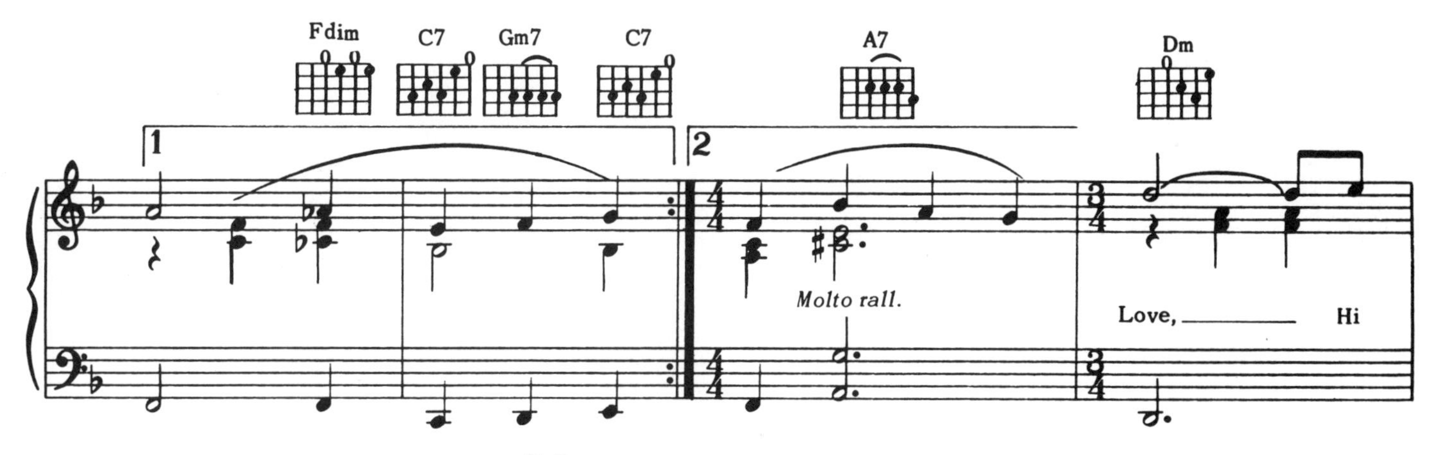
Fdim
C7
Gm7
C7
A7
Dm
1
2
Molto rall.
Love, Hi

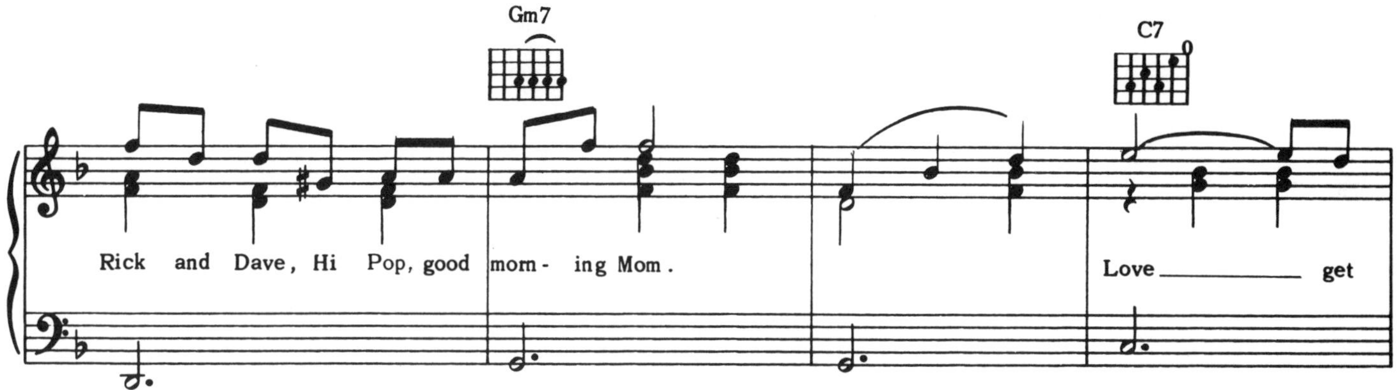
Gm7
C7
Rick and Dave, Hi Pop, good morn - ing Mom. Love get

Verse (2)
Patti Page and summer days, on old Cape Cod;
Happy times making wine, in my garage.
Country shade and lemonade, Guess, I'm slowing down;
It's a turn back world with a local girl in a smaller town,
Open cars and clearer stars, That's what I lack,
But fantasy world and Disney Girls, I'm coming back.

Verse (3)
All my life I've spent the nights with dreams of you;
And the warmth I missed and for the things I wished,
They're all coming true.
I've got my love to give and a place to live, Guess I'm gonna stay;
It'd be a peaceful life with a forever wife and a kid someday.
Well, It's early nights and pillow fights, and your soft laugh,
Oh, Fantasy world and Disney Girls, I'm coming back.

YOU'RE SO GOOD TO ME

Words & Music by Brian Wilson

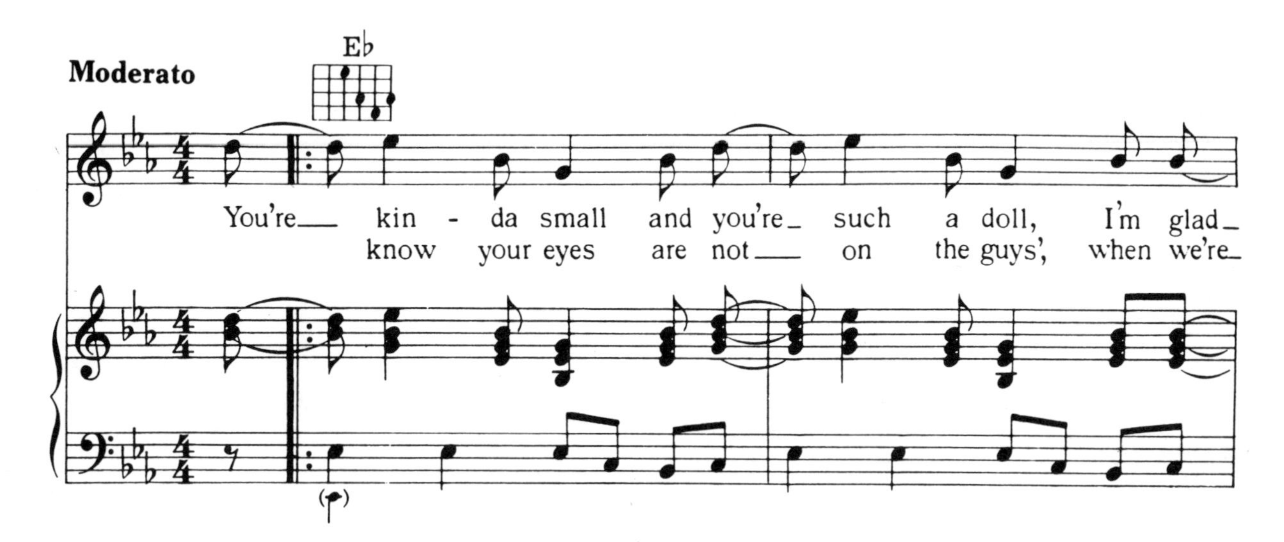

E♭
take my hand and you un - der- stand when I
ev' - ry night you hold me so tight when I

F
B♭7
get in a bad mood You're so good to me
kiss you good-bye You're so good to me

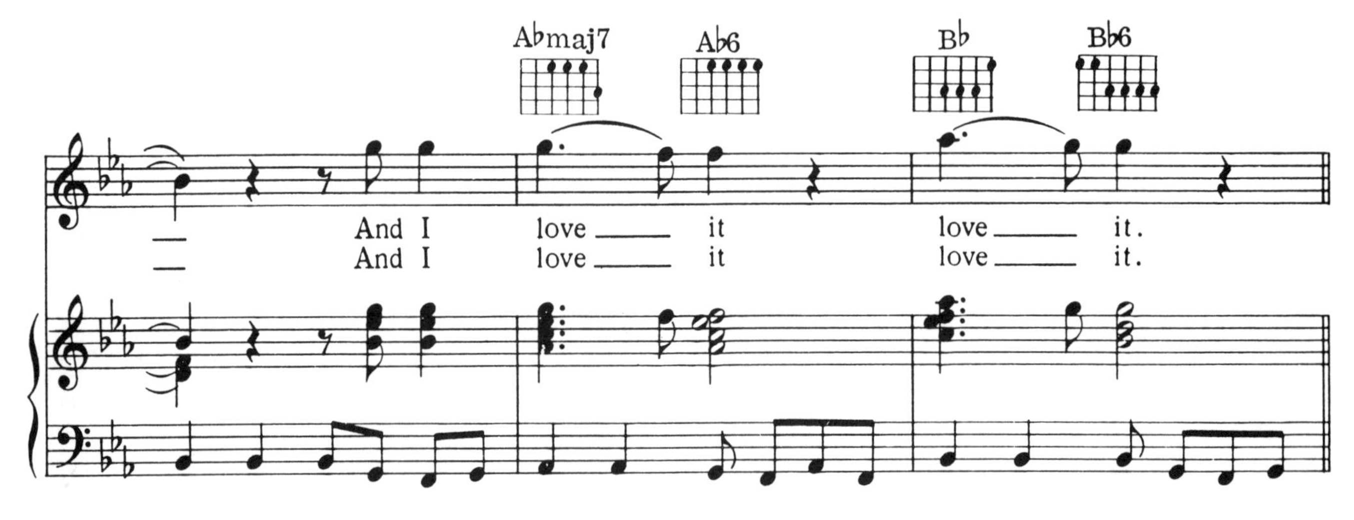
A♭maj7
A♭6
B♭
B♭6
And I love it love it.
And I love it love it.

E♭
La la la la la la la la la la la la la la la la
You're my ba -

Fm
La la la la la la la la la la la la la la la la
- by oh yeah Don't mean may -

E♭
La la la la la la la la la la la la la la la la
- be oh yeah

1 B♭11
B♭7
La la la la la la la la la la la la la la la la
I

2 B♭11
B♭7
D.𝄋 and fade
La la la la la la la la la la la la la la la la.

FRIENDS

Words & Music by Brian Wilson, Carl Wilson, Dennis Wilson & Al Jardine

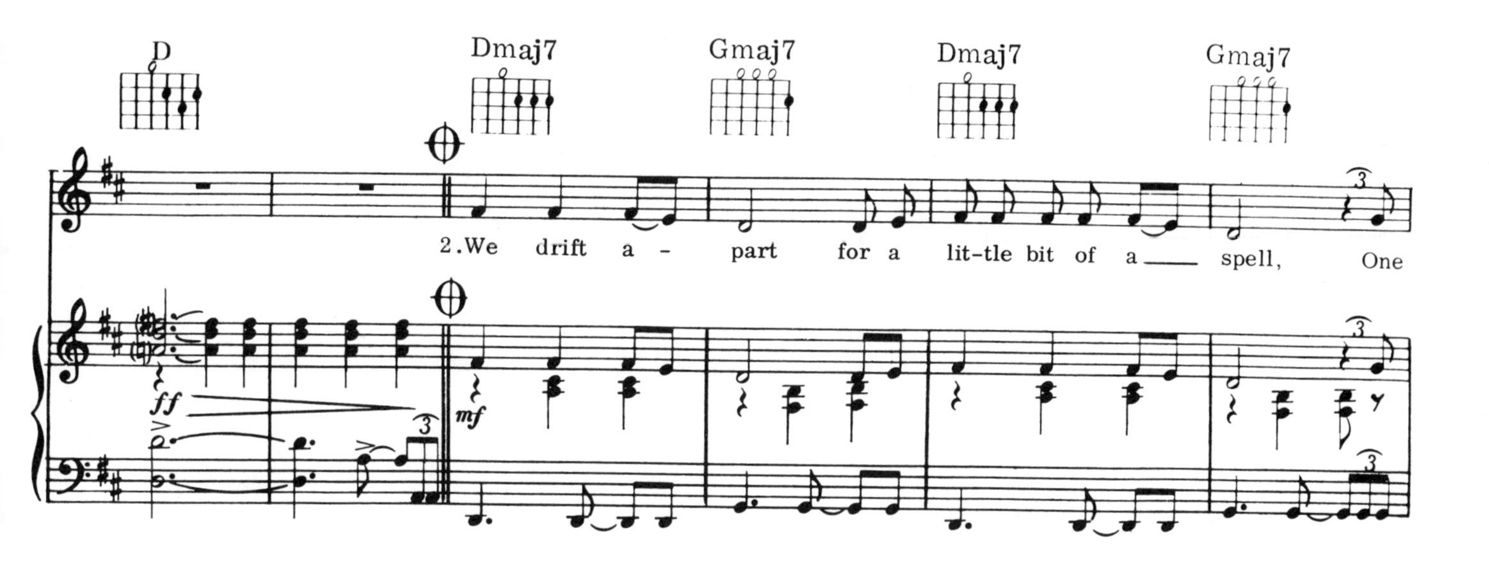
D
Dmaj7
Gmaj7
Dmaj7
Gmaj7
2.We drift a - part for a lit-tle bit of a spell, One
ff
mf

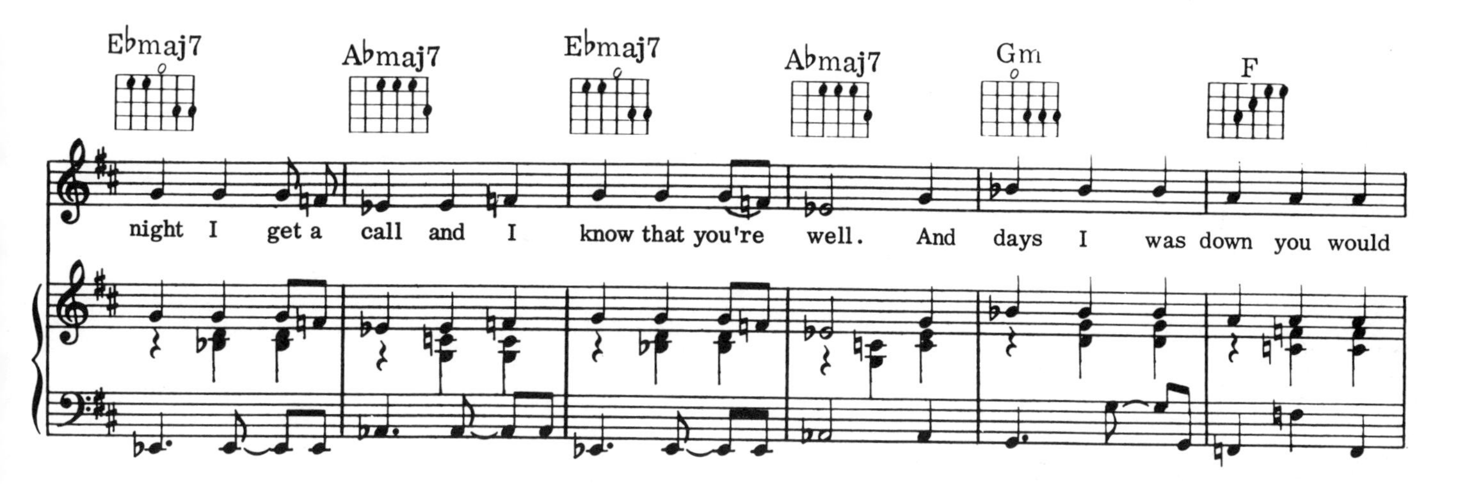
E♭maj7
A♭maj7
E♭maj7
A♭maj7
Gm
F
night I get a call and I know that you're well. And days I was down you would

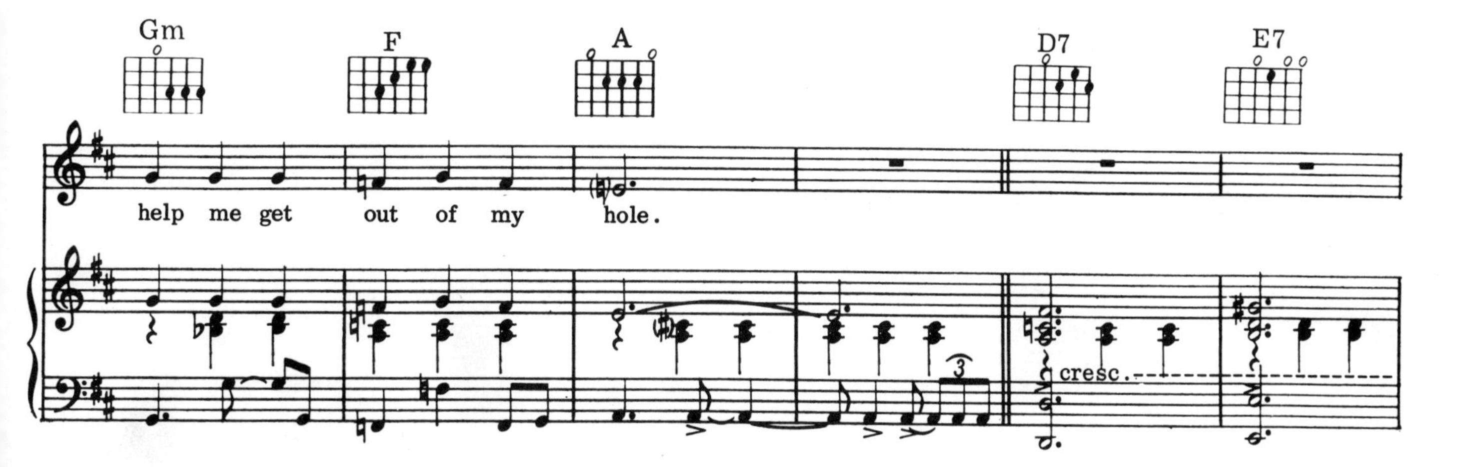
Gm
F
A
D7
E7
help me get out of my hole.
cresc.

G7
A7
C7
D7
Em7
Bm
(Ah)
ff
mf

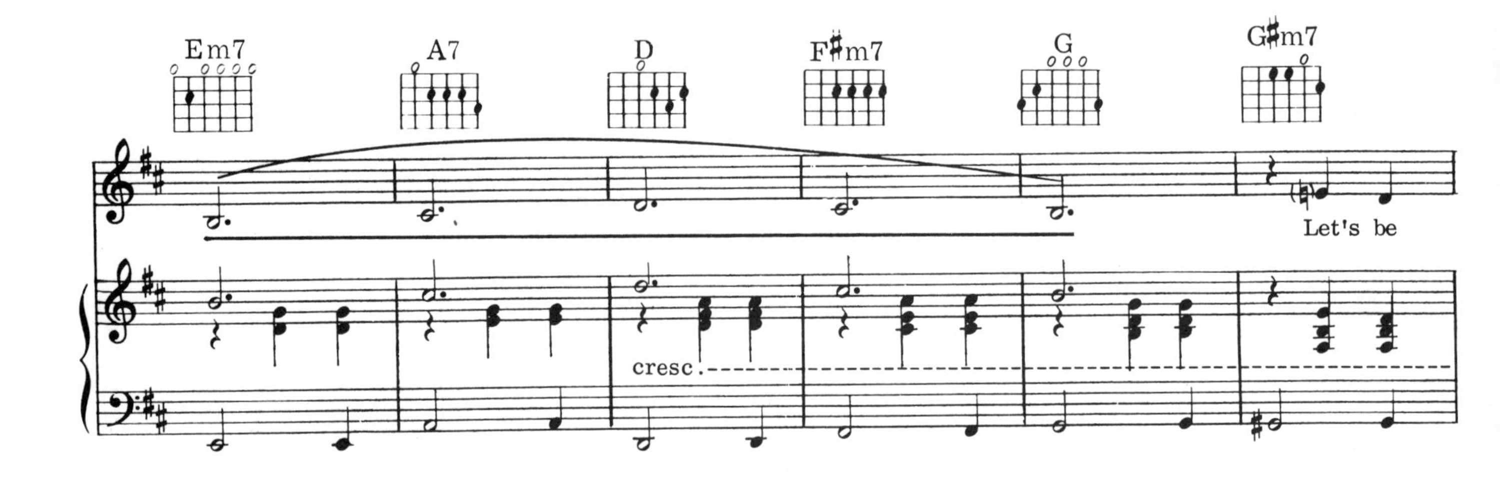
Em7
A7
D
F♯m7
G
G♯m7
Let's be
cresc.

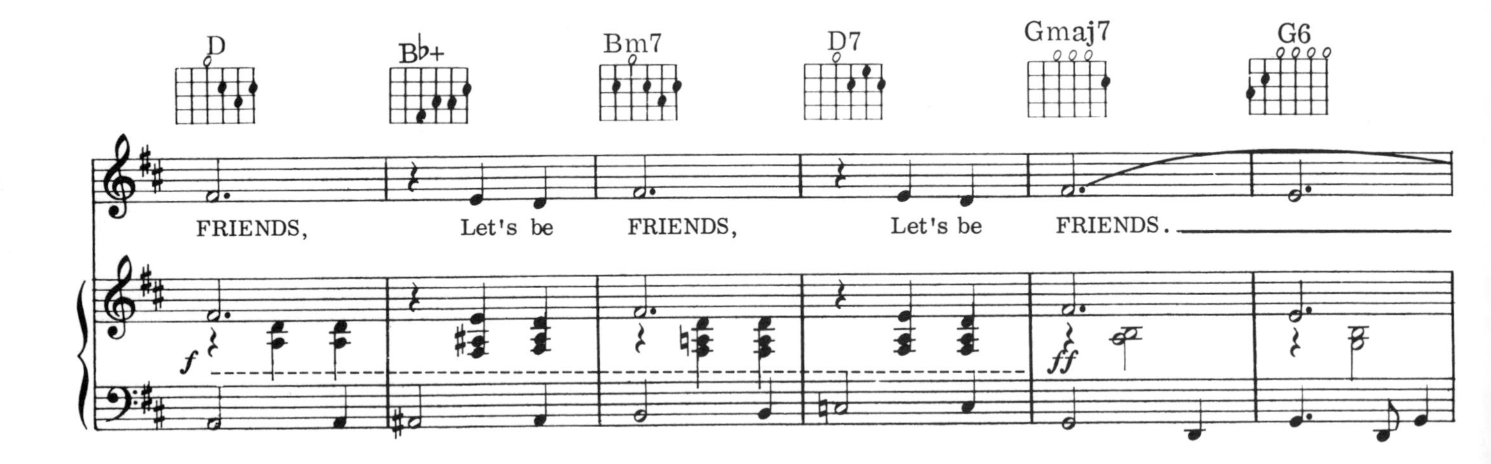
D
B♭+
Bm7
D7
Gmaj7
G6
FRIENDS,
Let's be
FRIENDS,
Let's be
FRIENDS.
f
ff

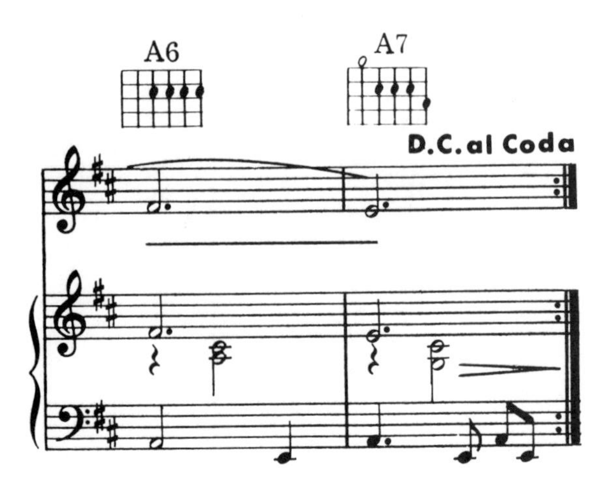
A6
A7
D.C. al Coda

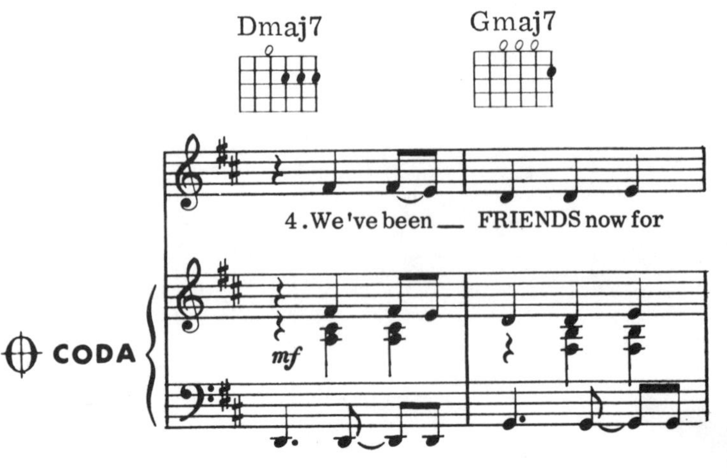
CODA
Dmaj7
Gmaj7
4. We've been FRIENDS now for
mf

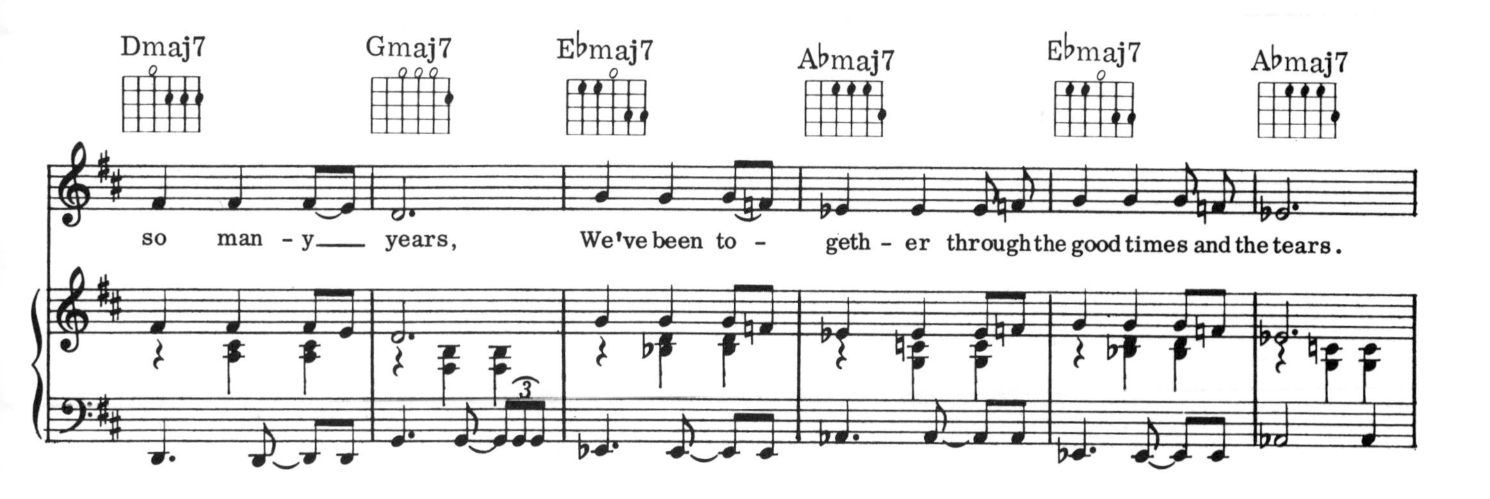
Dmaj7
Gmaj7
E♭maj7
A♭maj7
E♭maj7
A♭maj7
so man - y___ years, We've been to - geth - er through the good times and the tears.

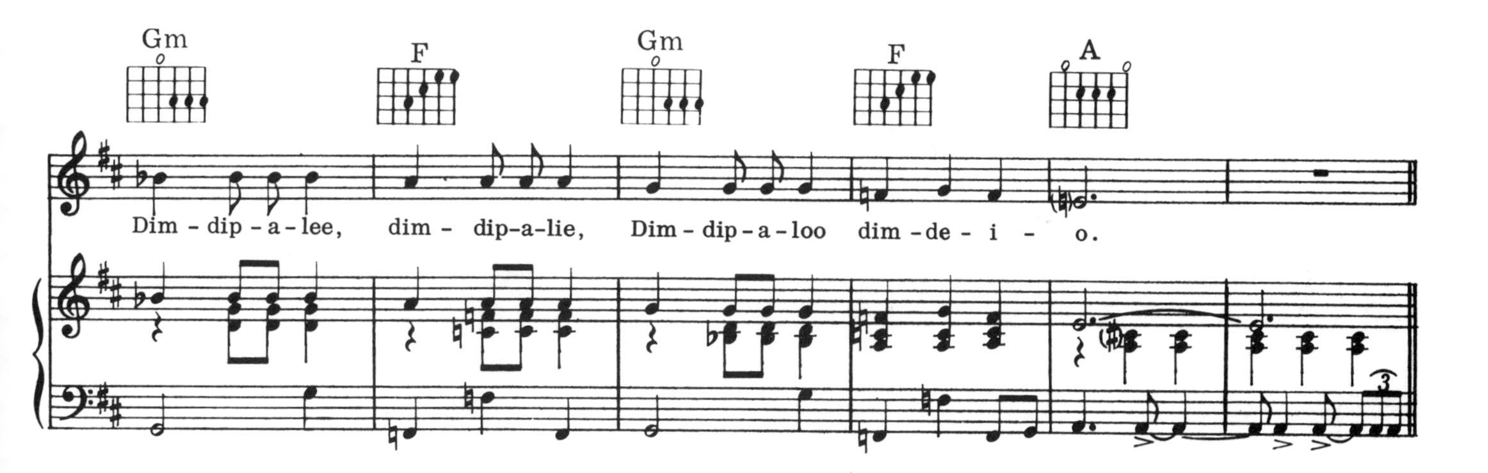
Gm
F
Gm
F
A
Dim - dip - a - lee, dim - dip-a-lie, Dim - dip - a - loo dim - de - i - o.

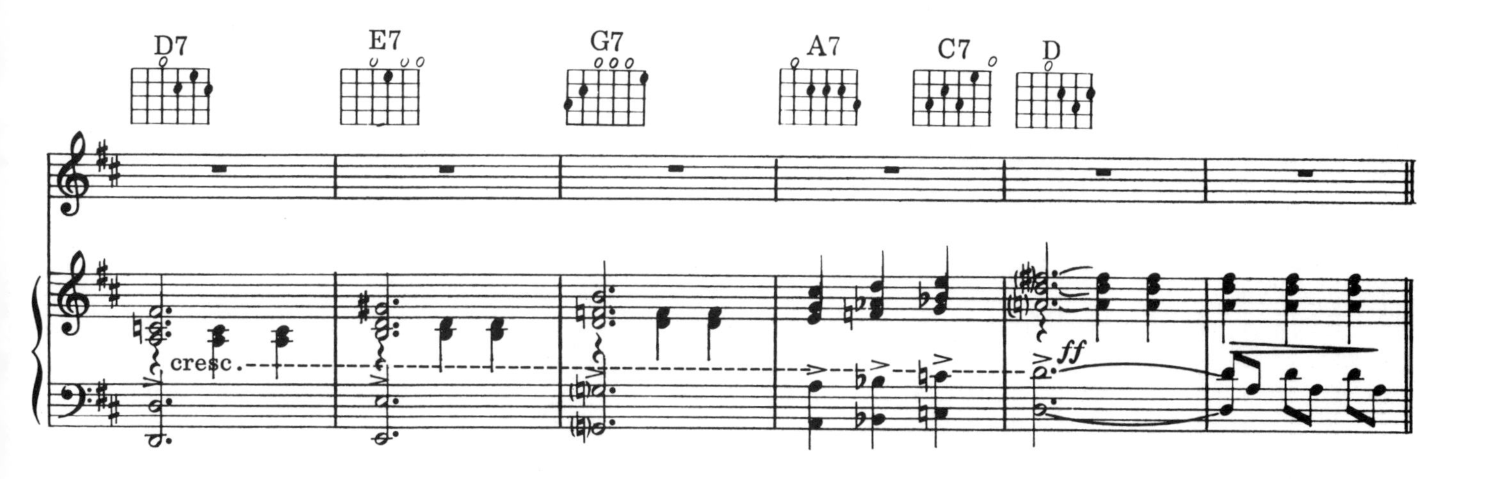
D7
E7
G7
A7
C7
D
cresc.
ff

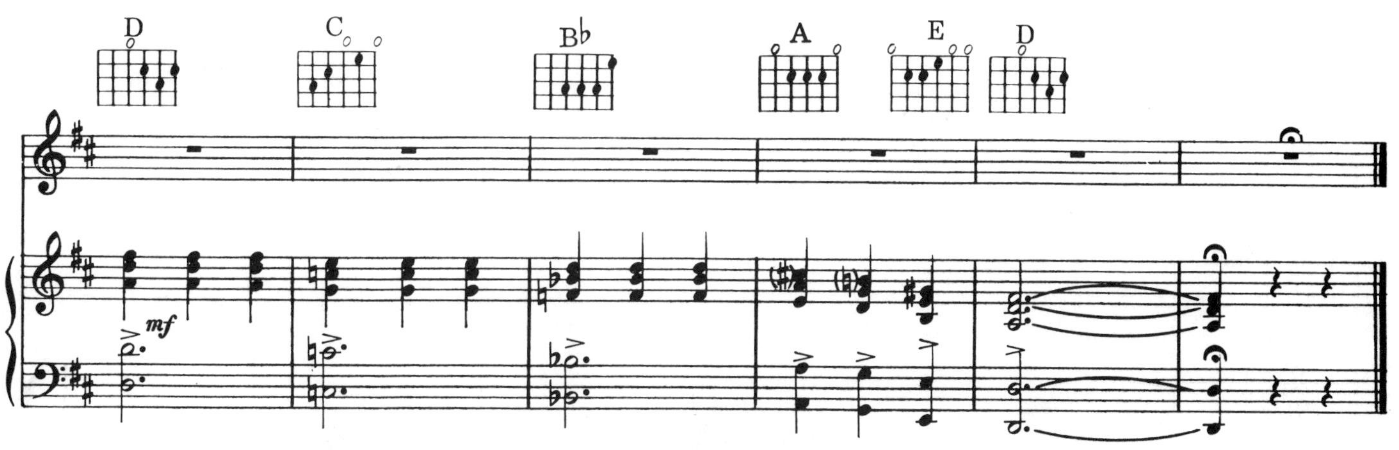
D
C
B♭
A
E
D
mf

HEROES AND VILLAINS

Words & Music by Brian Wilson & Van Dyke Parks

CHORUS
Dm
He - roes and Vil - lains, Just see what you done ——

G7
done.

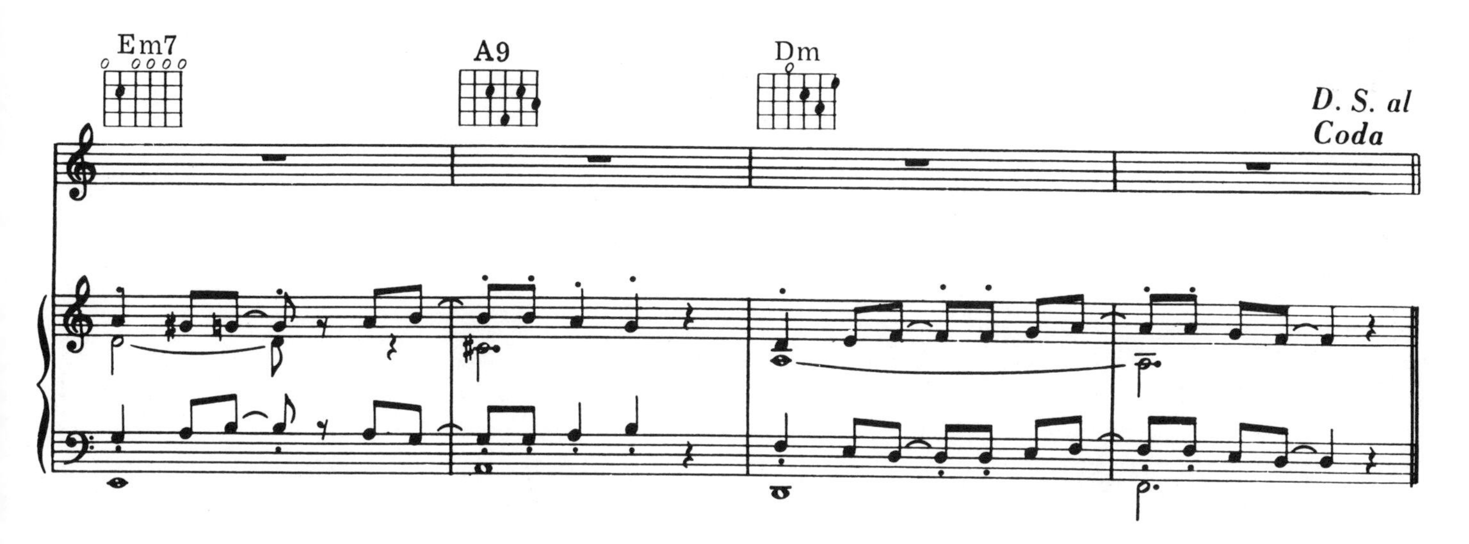
Em7
A9
Dm
D. S. al Coda

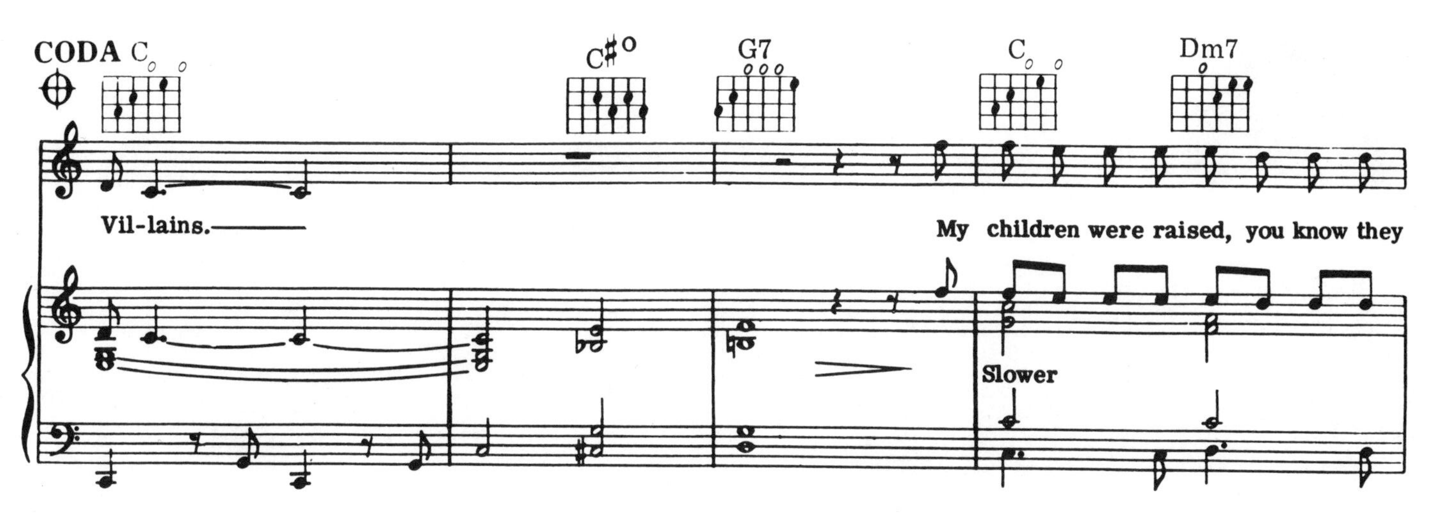
CODA
C
C♯o
G7
C
Dm7
Vil-lains.——
My children were raised, you know they
Slower

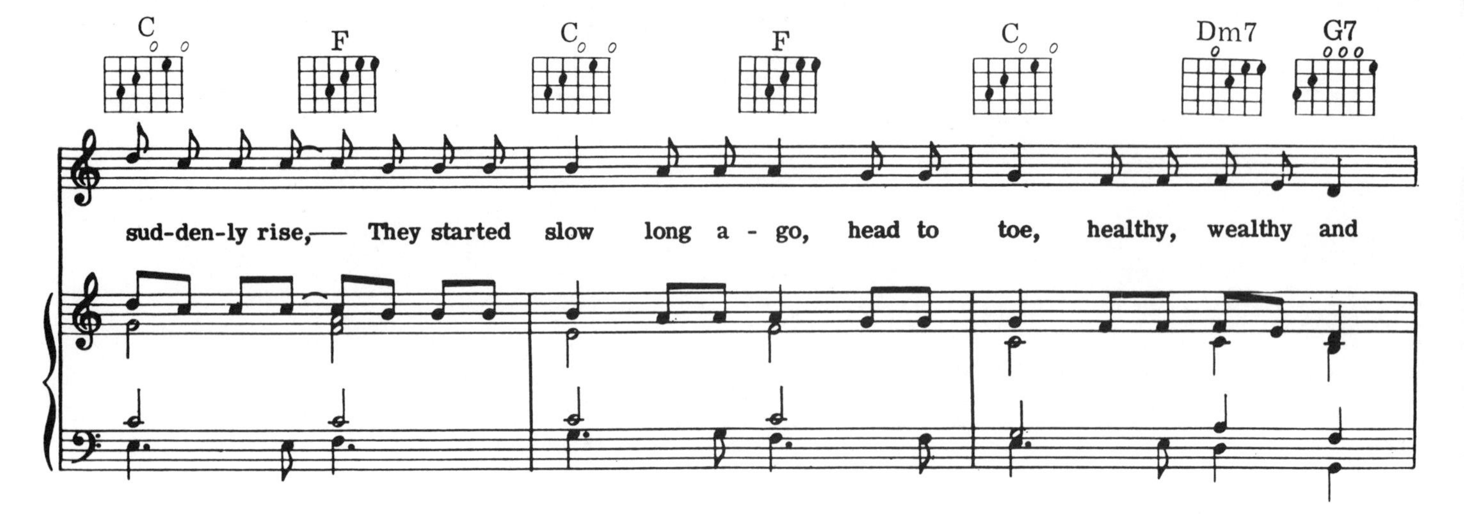
C
F
C
F
C
Dm7
G7
sud-den-ly rise,— They started slow long a - go, head to toe, healthy, wealthy and

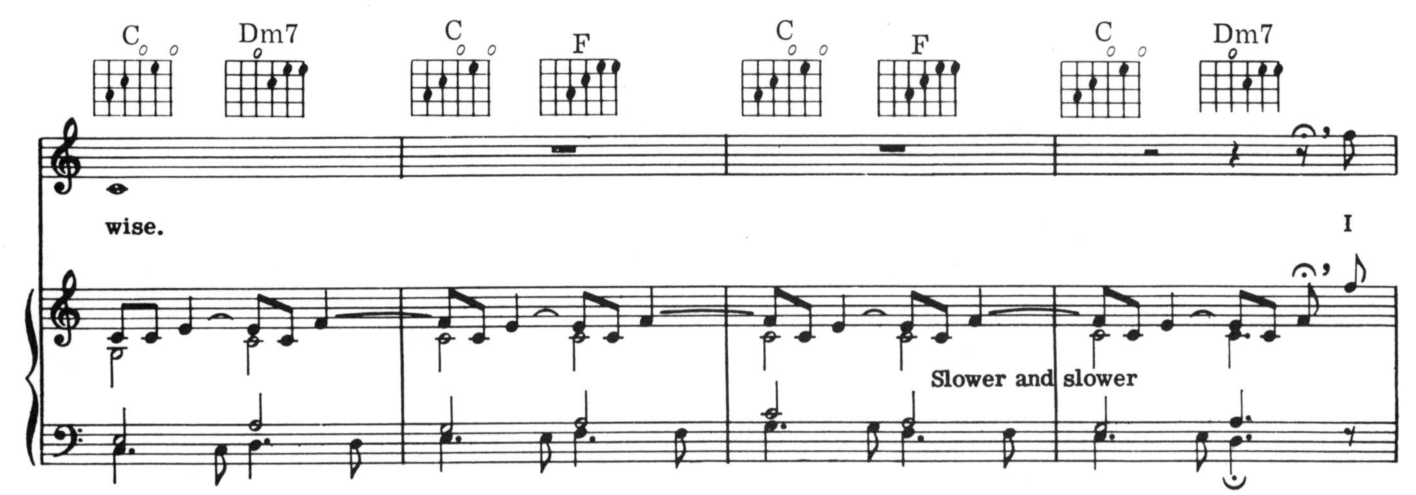
C
Dm7
C
F
C
F
C
Dm7
wise. I
Slower and slower

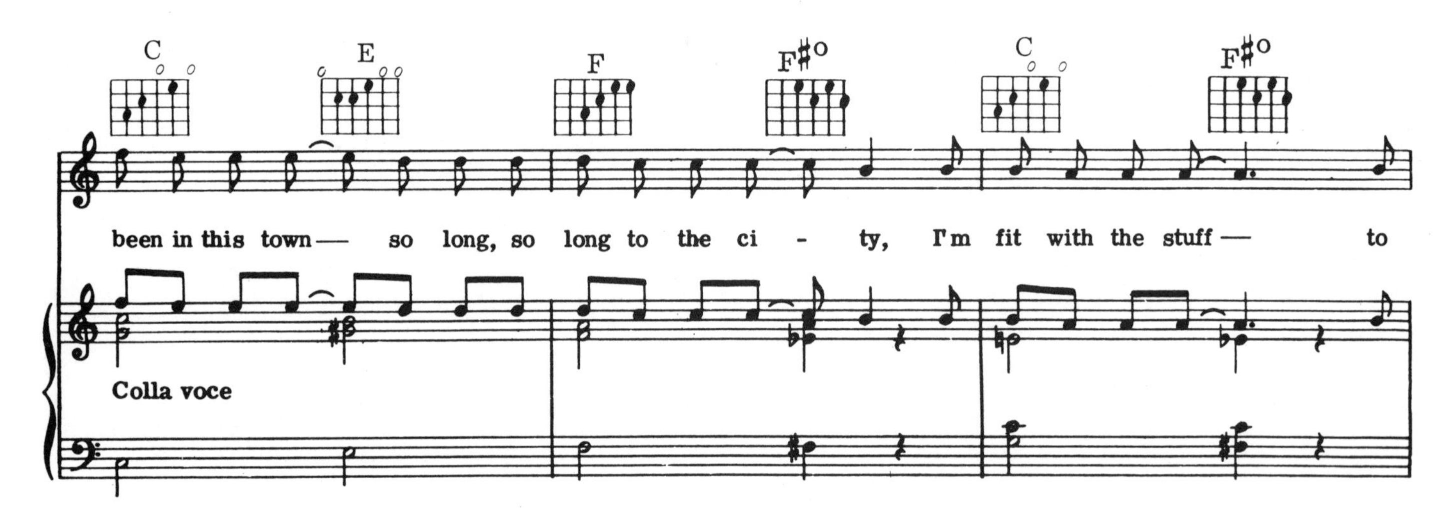
C
E
F
F#o
C
F#o
been in this town — so long, so long to the ci - ty, I'm fit with the stuff — to
Colla voce

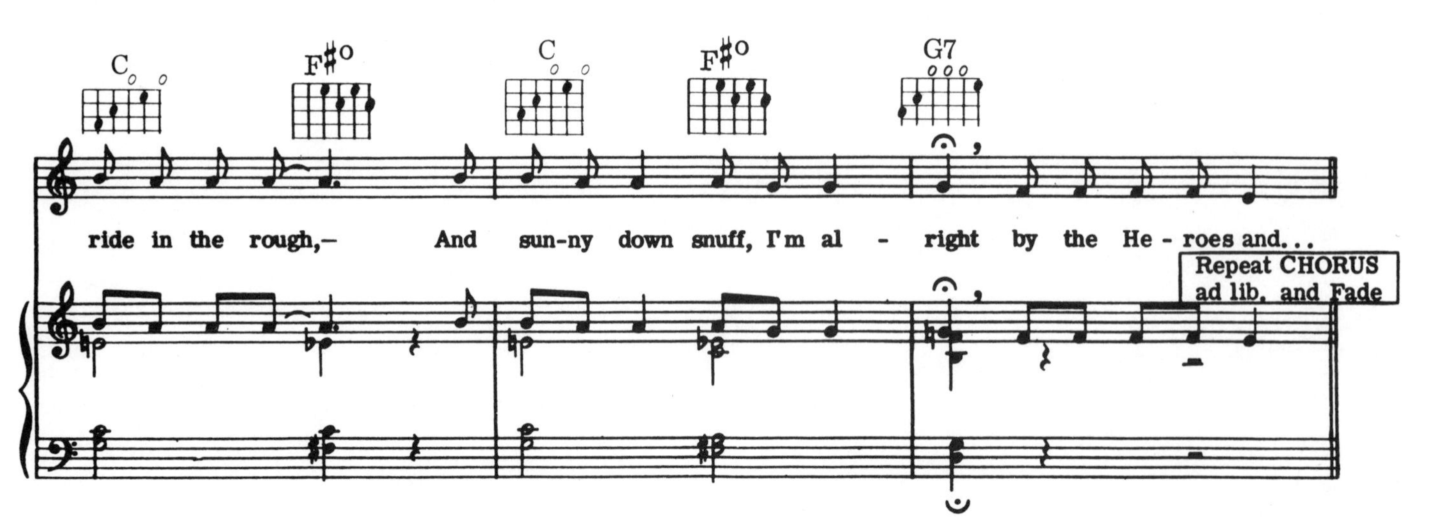
C
F#o
C
F#o
G7
ride in the rough,— And sun-ny down snuff, I'm al - right by the He - roes and...
Repeat CHORUS ad lib. and Fade

DO IT AGAIN

Words & Music by Brian Wilson & Mike Love

Sun - tanned bod-ies and waves of sun - shine, The Cal- i - for-nia girls and a
Ab
Bb
beau-ti-ful coast-line with warmed up wea - ther, Let's get to - geth- er and
Eb
Ab
Do it a-gain. —
With a
p subito
con pedale
Cm7
Fm7
girl the lone - ly sea looks good with moon light,

A♭
Gm
Fm7
Makes your night times warm and out of sight.
Cresc
B♭7
E♭
Well I've been think - ing 'bout all the pla - ces we've
f
surfed and danced, And all the fac - es we've missed, So let's get
A♭
B♭
E♭
back to - geth - er and Do it a - gain

CHERRY CHERRY COUPÉ

Words & Music by Brian Wilson & Roger Christian

Bb7
nose and decked with lov - ers on the hood.
o - pen when I want with a so - len - oid sys - tem.
got e - nough room now to bare - ly seat two.
Eb
Cm
Eb
Go, Cher - ry Cher - ry Coupe now, Go, Cher - ry Cher - ry
Cm
Ab
Coupe now, Go, Cher - ry Cher - ry Coupe now. Why don't you
1
2
3
D. 𝄋 and Fade
Bb7
Bbsus4
Bb
Bbsus4
Bb
Bbsus4
Bb
go, Cher - ry Cher - ry Coupe now. Coupe now. My Coupe now.

DON'T GO NEAR THE WATER

Words & Music by Al Jardine & Mike Love

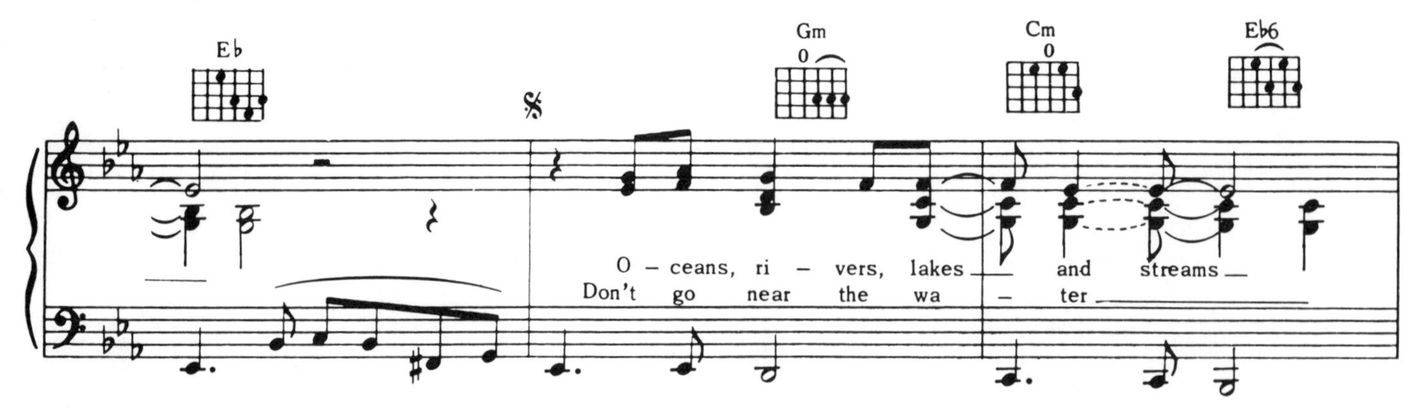

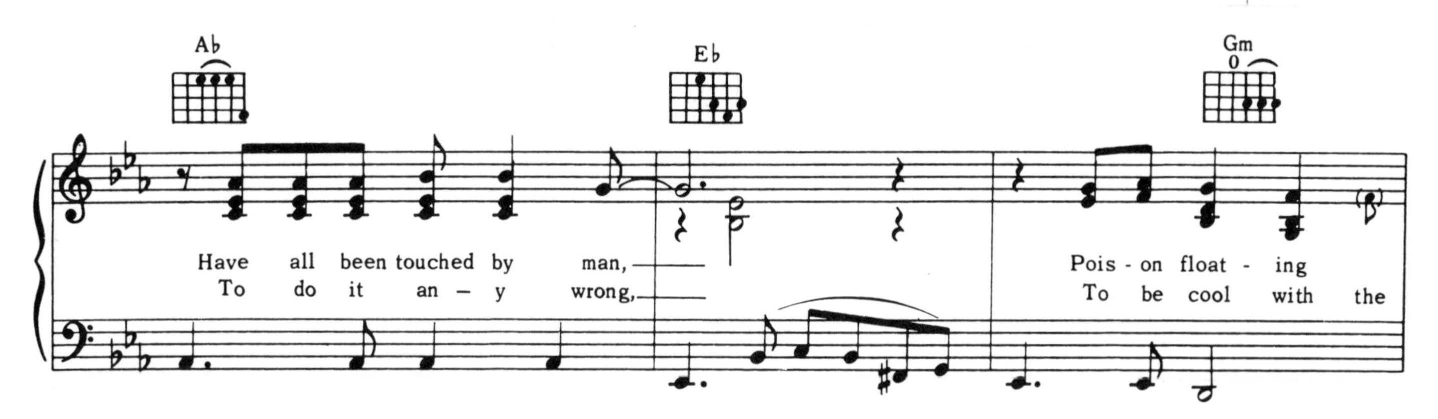

Ab
Eb
Gm
Have all been touched by man,
To do it an-y wrong,
Pois-on float-ing
To be cool with the

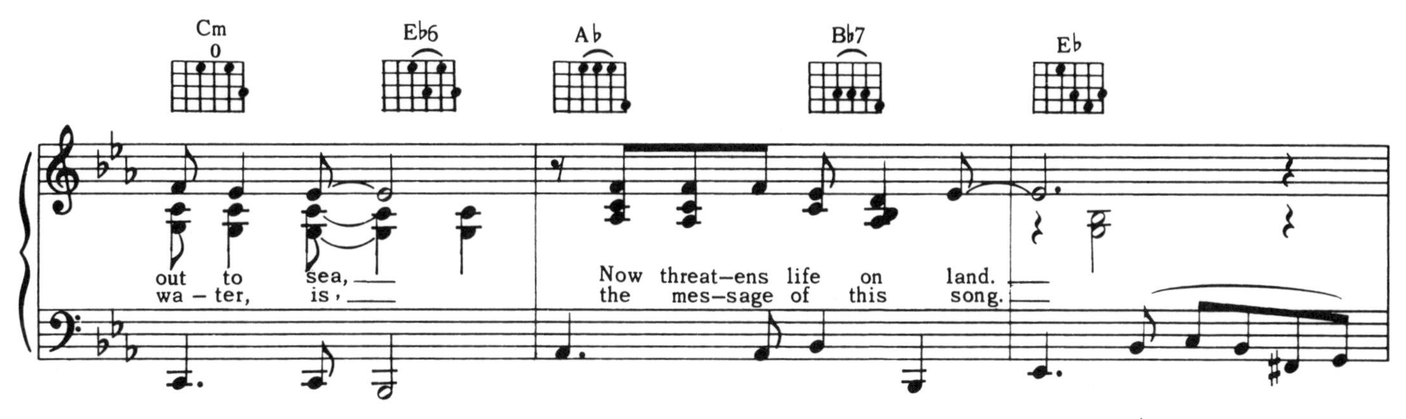

Cm
Eb6
Ab
Bb7
Eb
out to sea,
wa-ter, is,
Now threat-ens life on land.
the mes-sage of this song.

Ab
Don't go near the wa-ter,
Let's all help the wa-ter,
Ain't it
Right a-

Eb
sad
-way,
What's hap-pened to the wa-ter.
Do what we can and ought to.

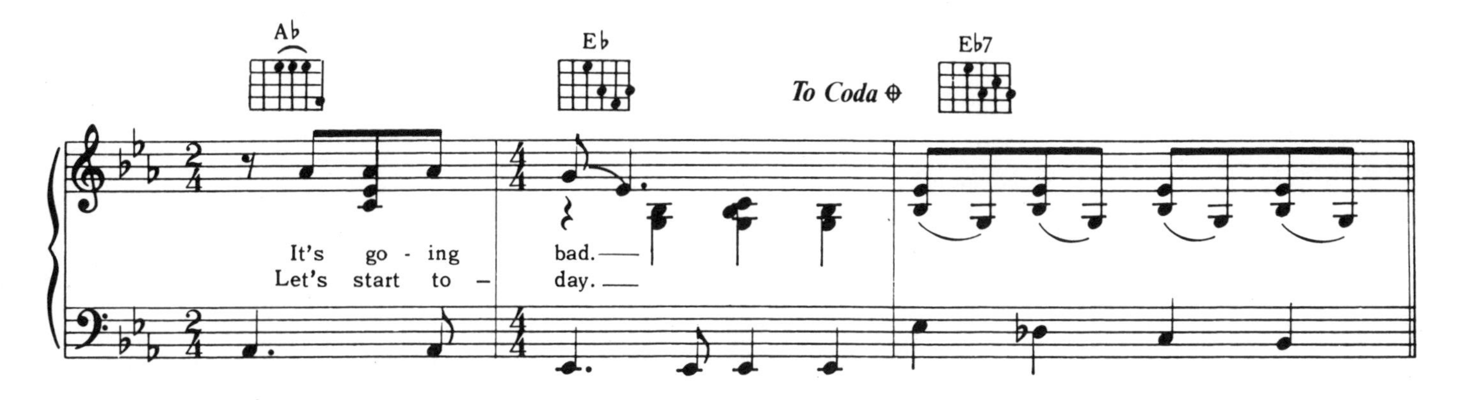

Ab
Eb
To Coda ⊕
Eb7
It's go-ing bad.
Let's start to-day.

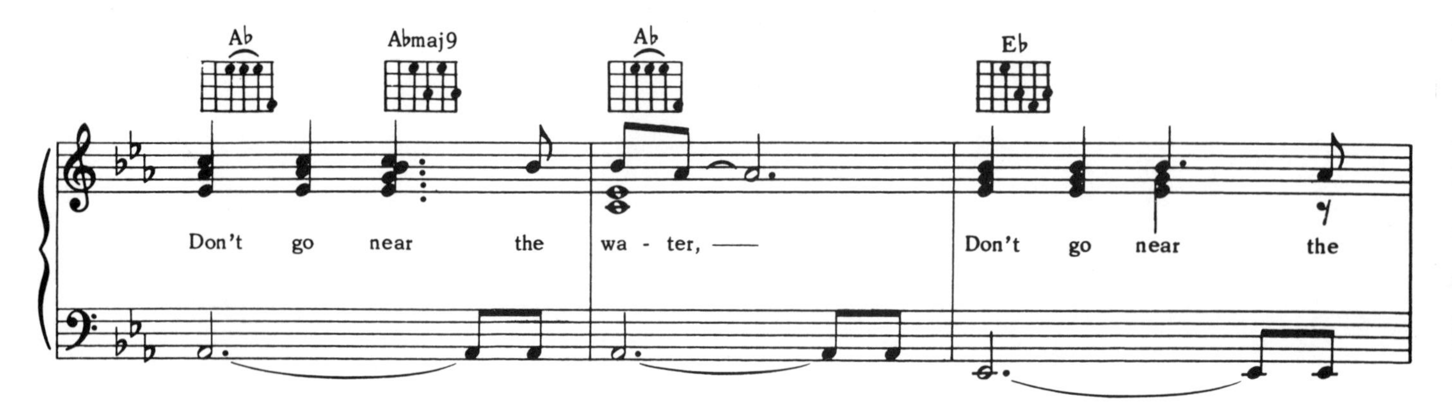
Ab
Abmaj9
Ab
Eb
Don't go near the wa - ter, — Don't go near the

Cm
Eb
Cm
wa - ter. — Tooth - paste and soap will make our o - ceans a bub — ble bath

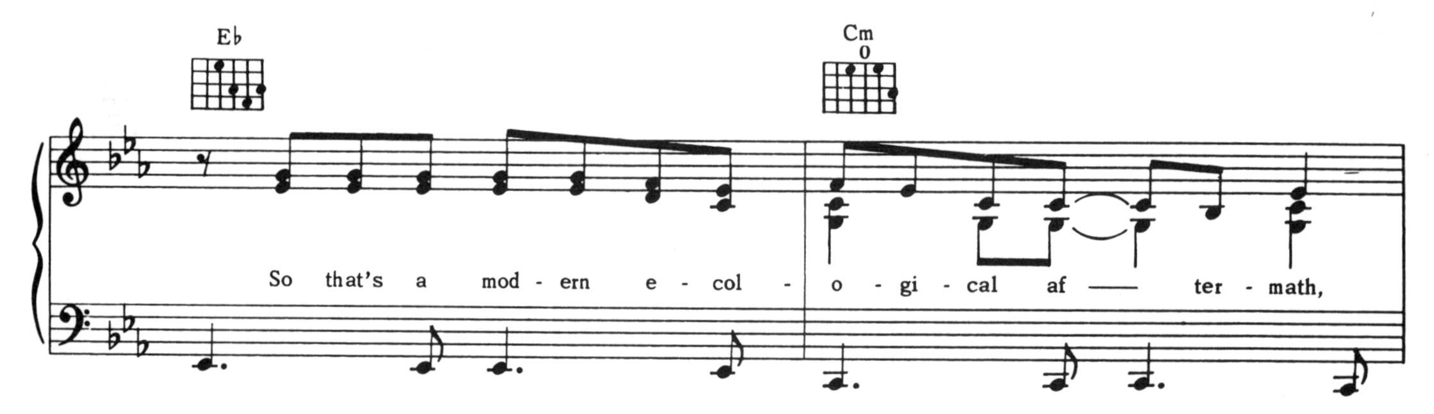
Eb
Cm
So that's a mod - ern e - col - o - gi - cal af — ter - math,

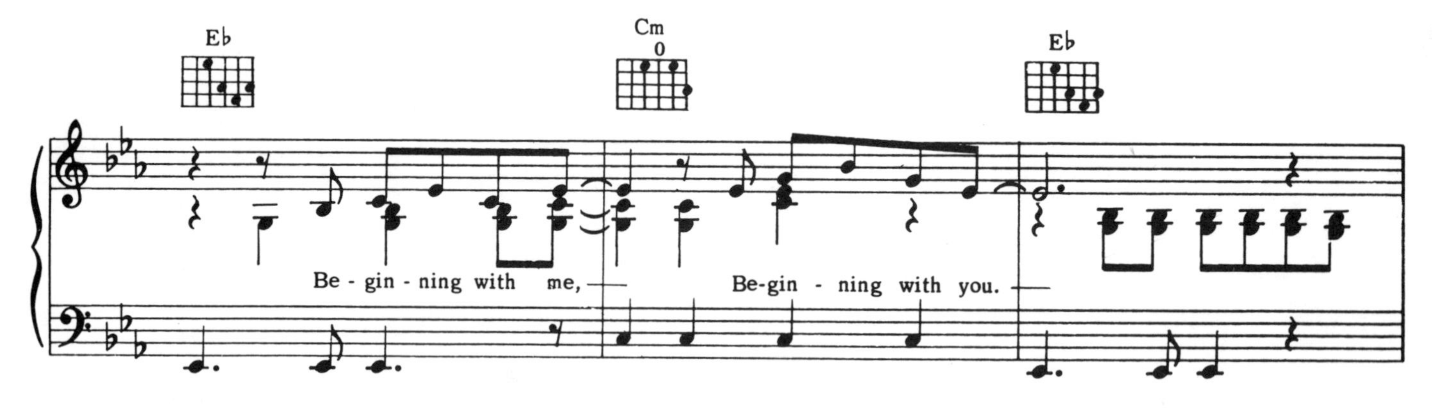
Eb
Cm
Eb
Be - gin - ning with me, — Be-gin - ning with you. —

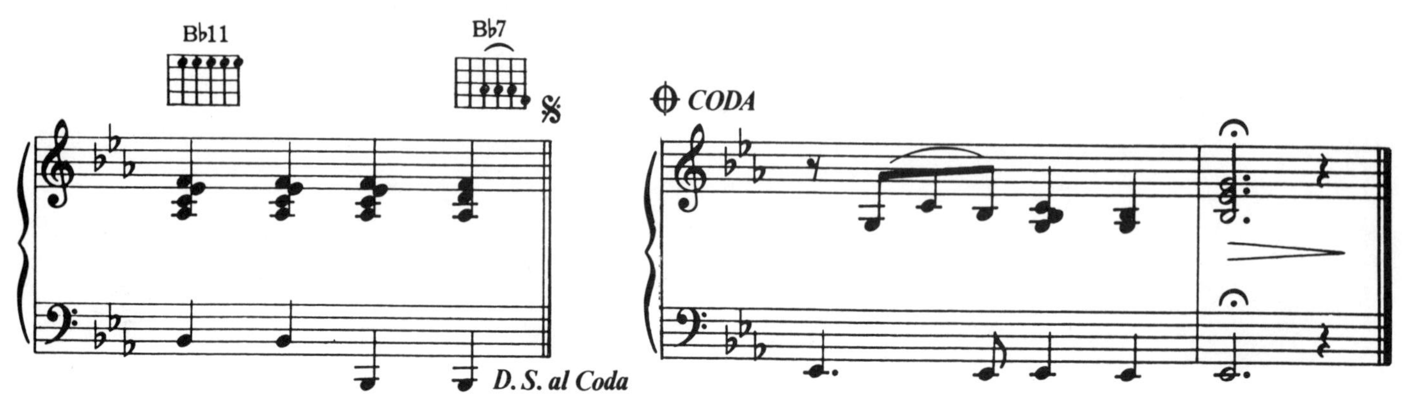
Bb11
Bb7
CODA
D.S. al Coda

HELP ME RHONDA

Words & Music by Brian Wilson

F
Rhon - da you look so fine, And I
Rhon - da you caught my eye, And I'll
Dm
D7
Gm7
know it would-n't take much time, For you to help me, Rhon - da,
give you lots of rea - sons why, You got - ta help me, Rhon - da,
C7
F
Help me get her out of my heart.
Help me get her out of my heart.
Chorus:
C7
F
HELP ME, RHON - DA! Help, HELP ME, RHON - DA! HELP ME, RHON - DA!
mf
C7
Help, HELP ME, RHON - DA! HELP ME, RHON - DA! Help, HELP ME, RHON - DA!

F
B♭
HELP ME, RHON - DA! Help, HELP ME, RHON - DA! HELP ME, RHON - DA!
F
Help, HELP ME, RHON - DA! HELP ME, RHON - DA! Help, HELP ME, RHON - DA!
Gm7
C9
1 F
HELP ME, RHON - DA! Yeah, get her out of my heart.
2. She was
mf
2 F
C7
HELP ME, RHON - DA!
f
F
Help, HELP ME, RHON - DA! HELP ME, RHON - DA! Help, HELP ME, RHON - DA!
Repeat till fadeout.

WOULDN'T IT BE NICE

Words & Music by Brian Wilson & Tony Asher

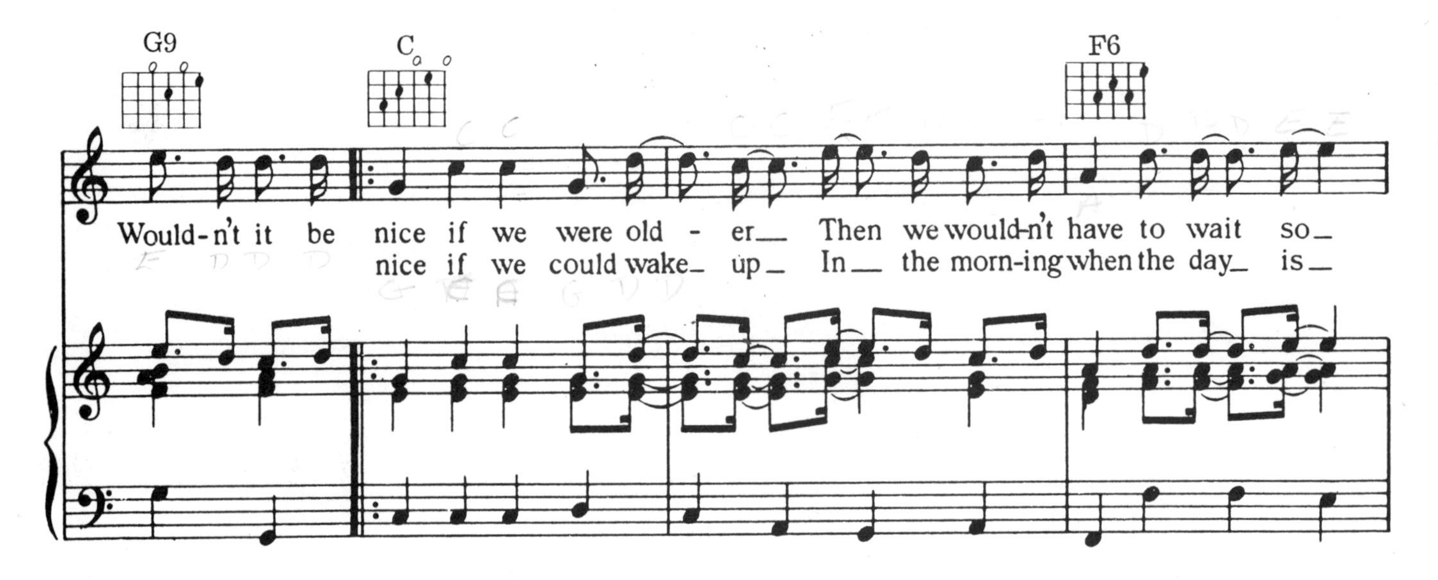

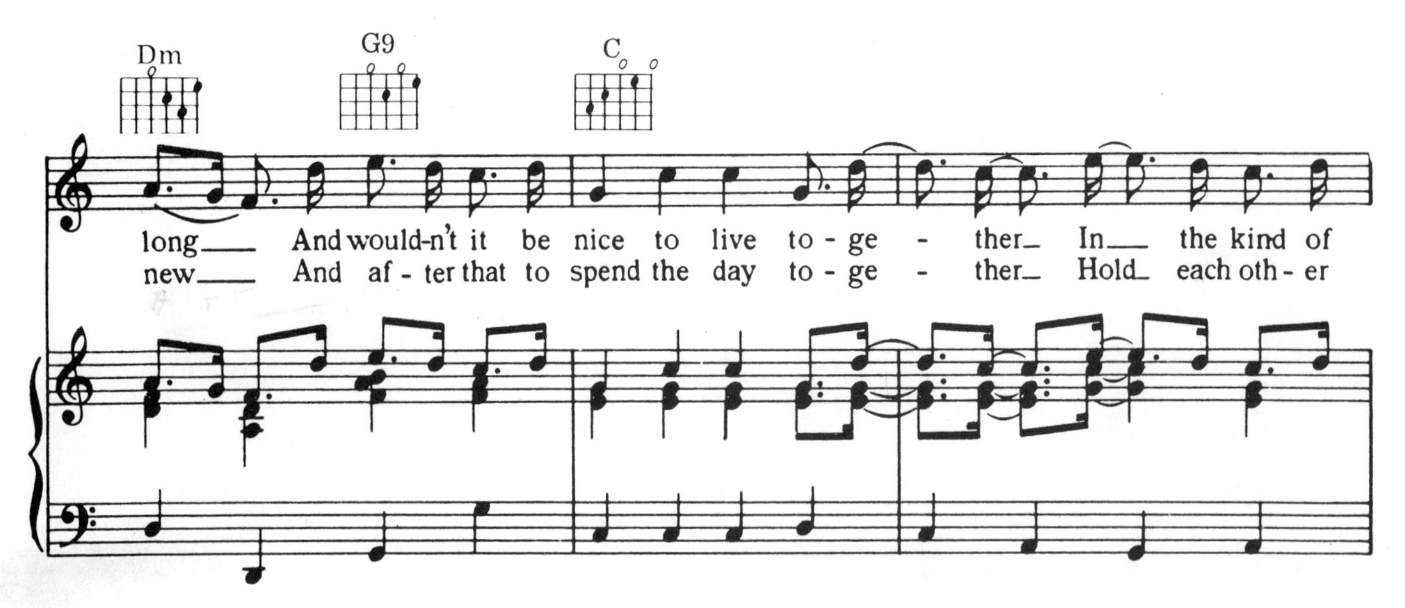

F6
Dm
G9
Am7
C11
world where we'd be - long
Though it's gon-na make it that much bet - ter
close the whole night through
The hap - py times to-geth-er we'd been spend-ing
Am
Em
Dm7
1
G9
When we can say good-night and stay to - geth - er
Would-n't it be
I wish that ev'- ry kiss was nev - er end - ing

2
G9
C
A
3
Oh would-n't it be nice
Well may-be if we
D
C♯m
F♯m7
A
think and wish and hope and pray it might come true
Ba-by then there

D
C♯m
F♯m7
would-n't be a sin-gle thing we could-n't do
We could be mar-
C♯m7
F♯m7
C♯m7
G9
-ried and then we'd be hap - py
Oh would-n't it be-

C
nice.

C
C
Am
You know it seems the more we

C11
Am
Em
talk a - bout it
If on - ly makes it worse to live with - out

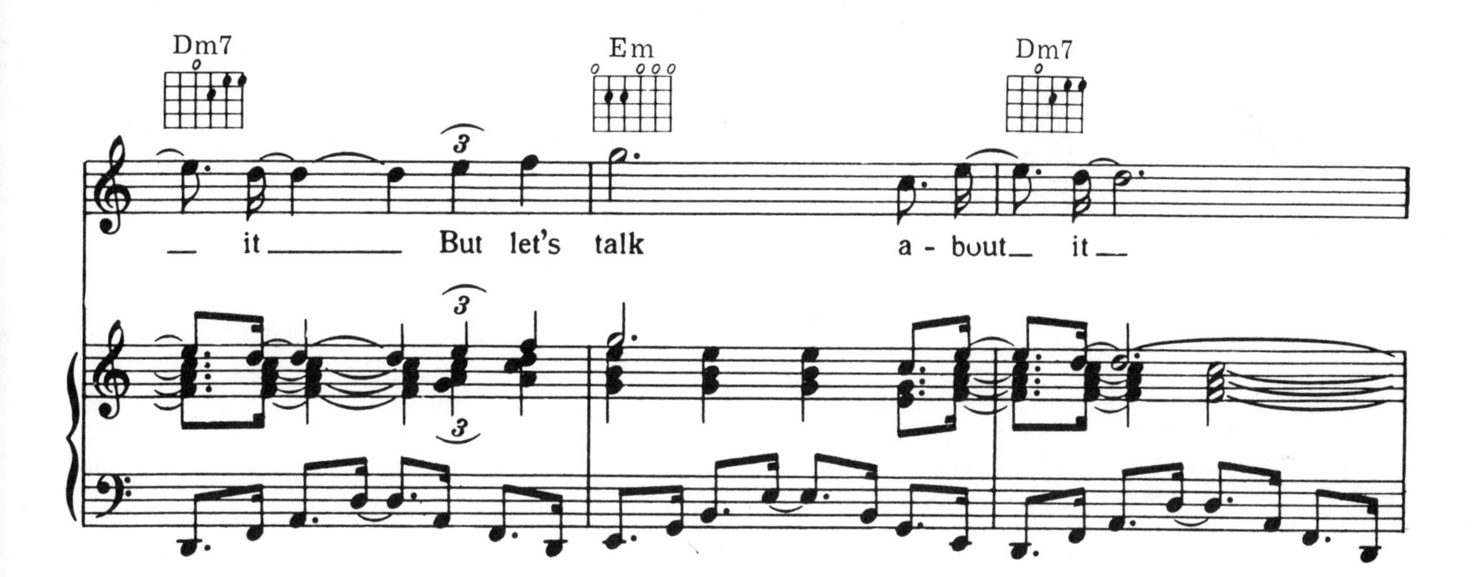
Dm7
Em
Dm7
it
But let's talk a - bout it

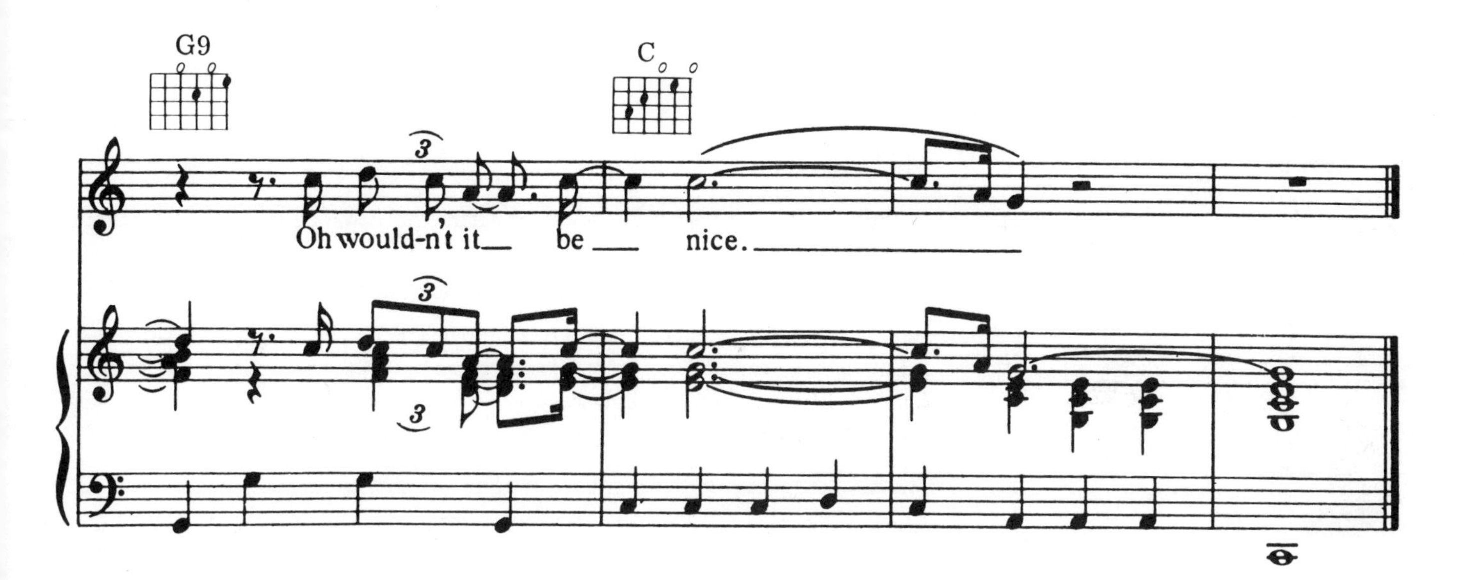
G9
C
Oh would-n't it be nice.

DARLIN'

Words & Music by Brian Wilson & Mike Love

Cm7
F
F9
B♭
precious part —
out of sight —
Oh ———
Oh ———
dar lin' ——— I
dar lin' ——— I
E♭6
Gm
C7
dream about you often my
dream about you often my
pretty girl yeah ——— I
pretty girl yeah ——— I
love the way you sof-ten my
love the way you sof-ten my

B♭
B♭6
F7
E♭
1
life with your love your
life with your love your
precious love uh –
precious love uh –
huh ———
huh –

2
Fm7
E♭
F9
Oh ———
Dal Segno
& FADE ad lib.

CALIFORNIA GIRLS

Words & Music by Brian Wilson

Eb
F7
north-ern girls_ with_ the way__ they kiss_ They keep their boy-friends warm at__ night._
could-n't wait_ to__ get back in the states_ Back to the cut - est girls in the world._
Chorus
Bb
Cm7
Db
I wish they all could be__ Cal-i-for-nia, I wish they all could be__ Cal-i-for-nia, I
mf
Gb
B
1. Bb
wish they all could be__ CAL-I-FOR-NIA GIRLS.__ 2. The
2 Bb
GIRLS.__
I
f
L.H.
Bb
Eb
wish they all could be__ Cal-i-for-nia, I wish they all could be__ Cal-i-for-nia; I
mf Repeat till fade out

WIND CHIMES

Words & Music by Brian Wilson

E7
G
Bm
Wind Chimes, Wind Chimes. Close your eyes and lean back,

E7
G
E7
A
lis-ten to Wind Chimes, Wind Chimes. It's so peace-ful,

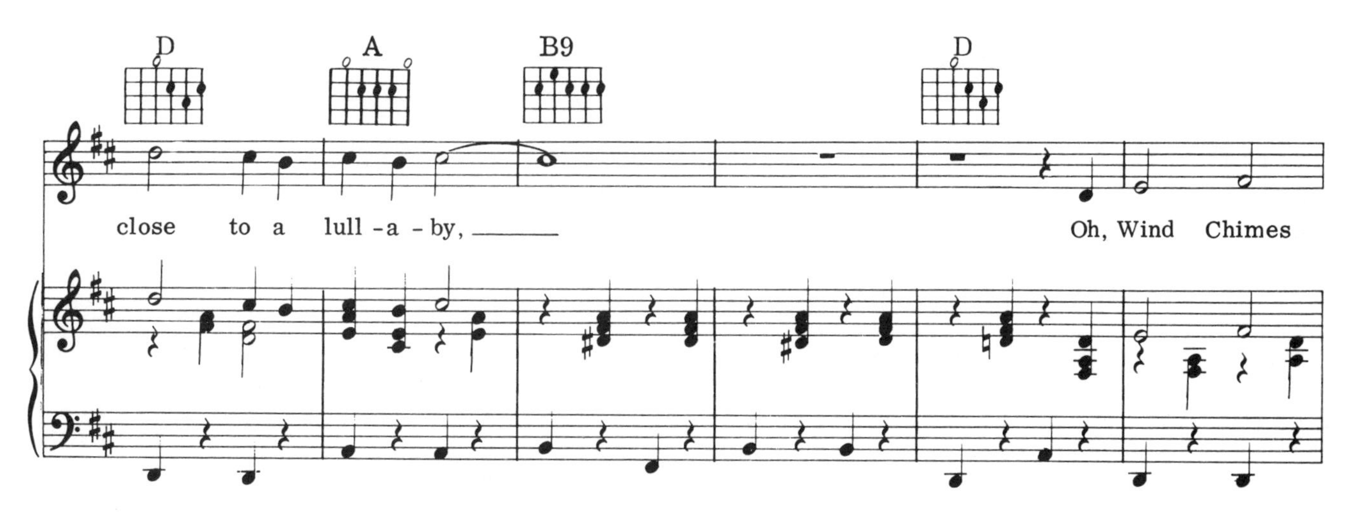
D
A
B9
D
close to a lull-a-by,
Oh, Wind Chimes

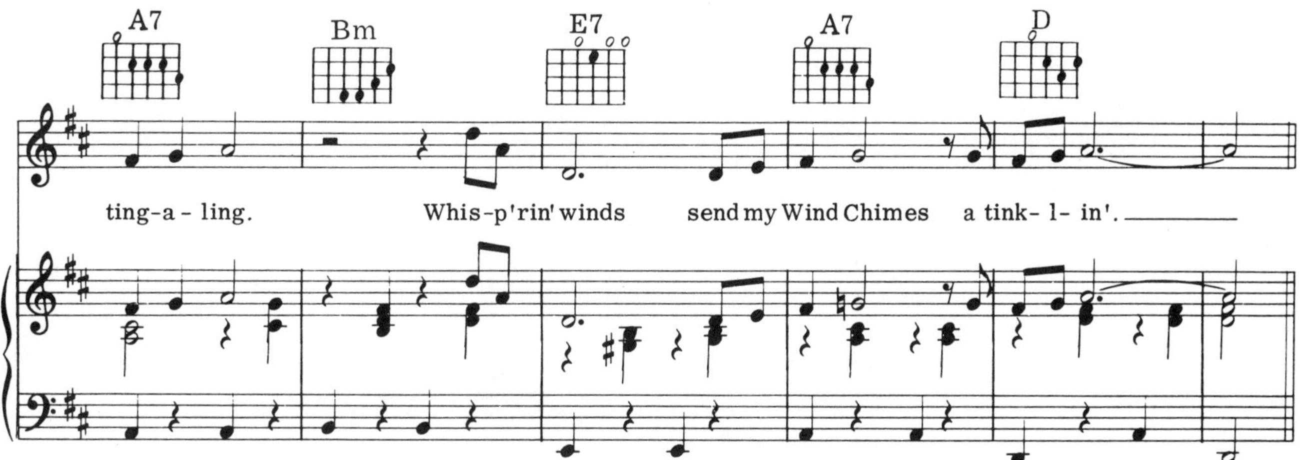
A7
Bm
E7
A7
D
ting-a-ling. Whis-p'rin' winds send my Wind Chimes a tink-l-in'.

GOD ONLY KNOWS

Words & Music by Brian Wilson & Tony Asher

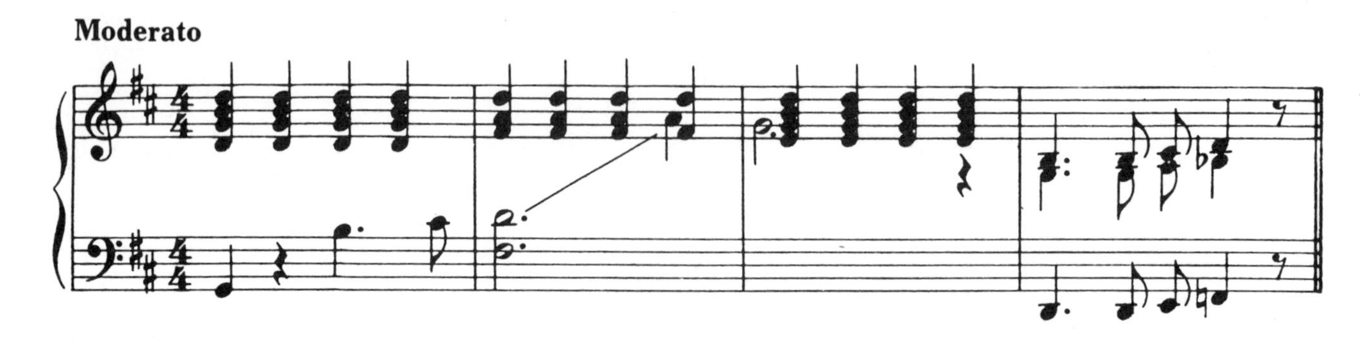

G
D
Em7
1 D
God on-ly knows what I'd be with-out you.
God on-ly knows what I'd be with-out you.

2 D
G
D
Repeat and fade
God on-ly knows what I'd be with-out

Em7
D
G
God on-ly knows what I'd be with-out
you.
God on-ly knows
you.

BARBARA ANN

Words & Music by Fred Fassert

F
F6
Went to a dance, look-in' for ro-mance, Saw Bar-bar Ann, so I
Played my fav-'rite tune, danced with Bet-ty Lou, Tried Peg-gy Sue, But I
mp
F6
F7
Bb
thought I'd take a chance.
knew they would-n't do.
Oh, Bar-bar Ann, Bar-bar Ann, take my hand. Oh, Bar-bar
mf
F
C7
Ann, Bar-bar Ann, take my hand. You got me rock-in' and a-roll-in', Rock-
Bb
F
in' and a-roll-in', Bar-bar Ann, Bar-bar-bar-bar-bar Ann.
D. C. al Fine

FUN FUN FUN

Words & Music by Brian Wilson & Mike Love

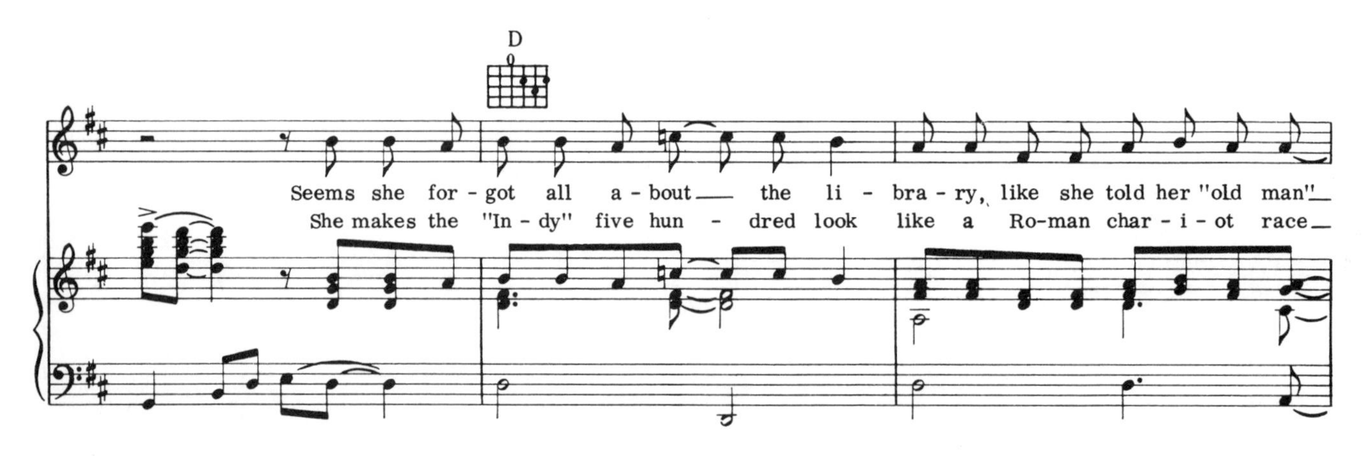

G
D
F♯m
cruis-in' just as fast as she can — now —
leads 'em on a wild - goose chase — now —
And she'll have FUN, FUN, FUN, till her

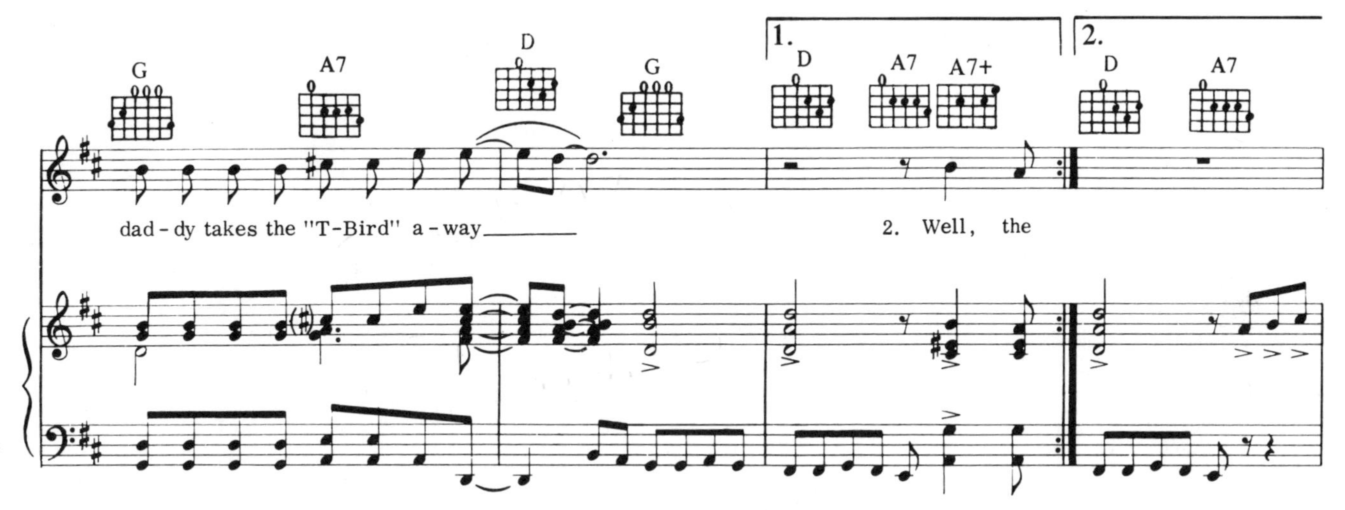
G
A7
D
G
1.
D
A7
A7+
2.
D
A7
dad - dy takes the "T-Bird" a - way
2. Well, the

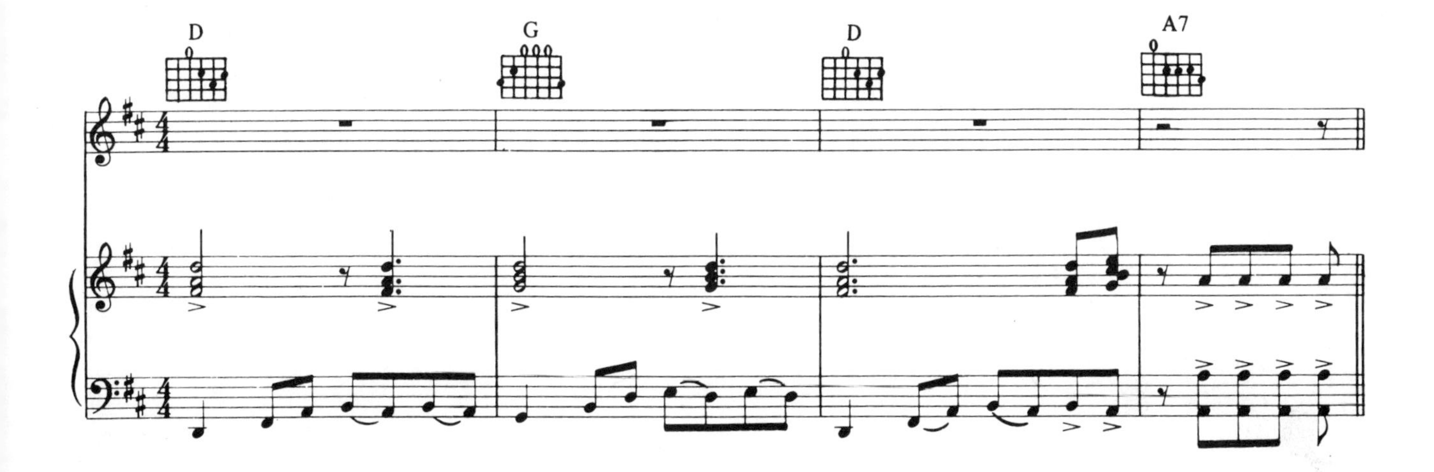
D
G
D
A7

D
G
(3rd Verse)
A-well, you knew all a - long — that your dad was get - tin' wise to you — Now —

D
And since he took your set of keys, you've been think-in' that your fun is all thru_
A7
A7+
D
now
But you can come along with me, 'cause we
G
got-ta lot-ta things to do now
And you'll have
D
F#m
G
A7
D
G
1.
D
A7+
FUN, FUN, FUN, now that dad-dy took the "T-Bird" a-way
And you'll have
2.
D
E7
A
D
G7
And you'll have FUN, FUN, FUN, now that dad-dy took the "T-Bird" a-way.
Keep repeating until fade-out

THAT'S NOT ME

Words & Music by Brian Wilson & Tony Asher

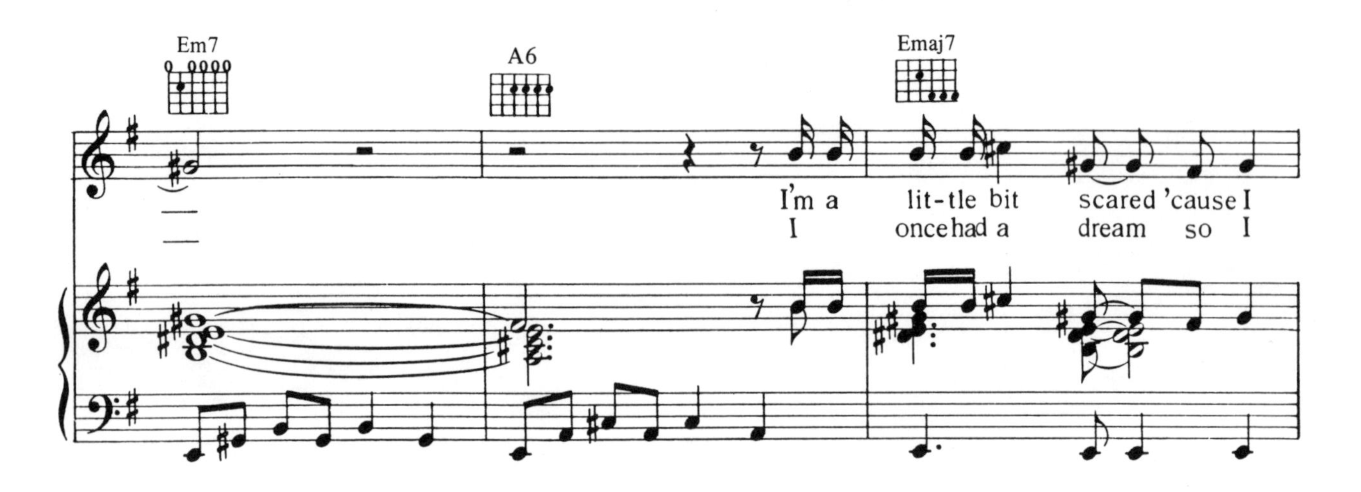
Em7
A6
Emaj7
I'm a lit-tle bit scared 'cause I
I once had a dream so I

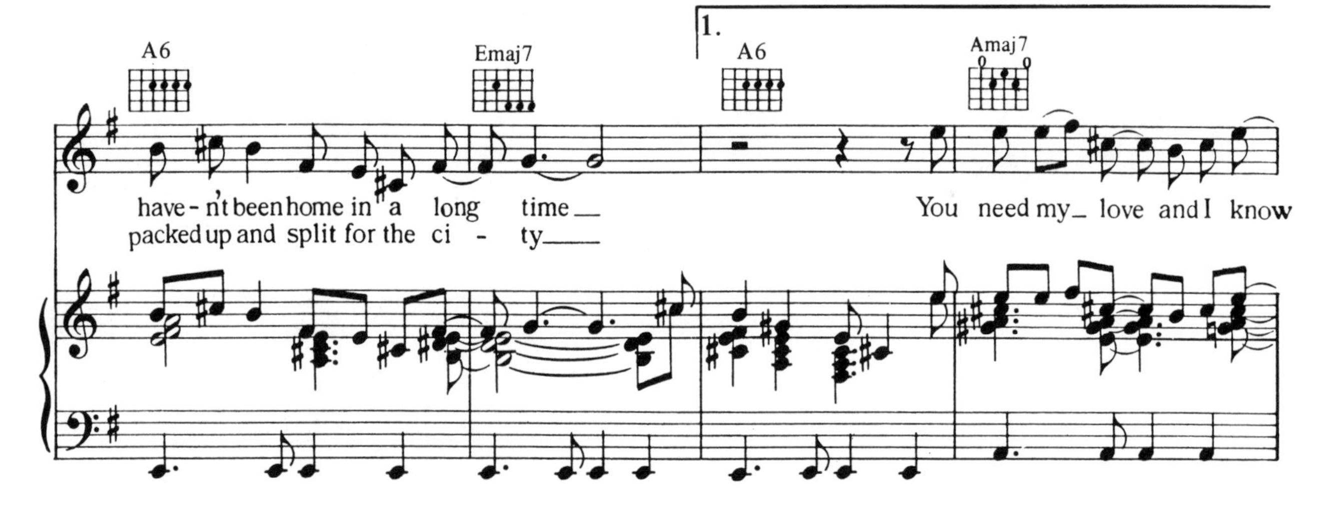
A6
Emaj7
1.
A6
Amaj7
have-n't been home in a long time
packed up and split for the ci - ty
You need my love and I know

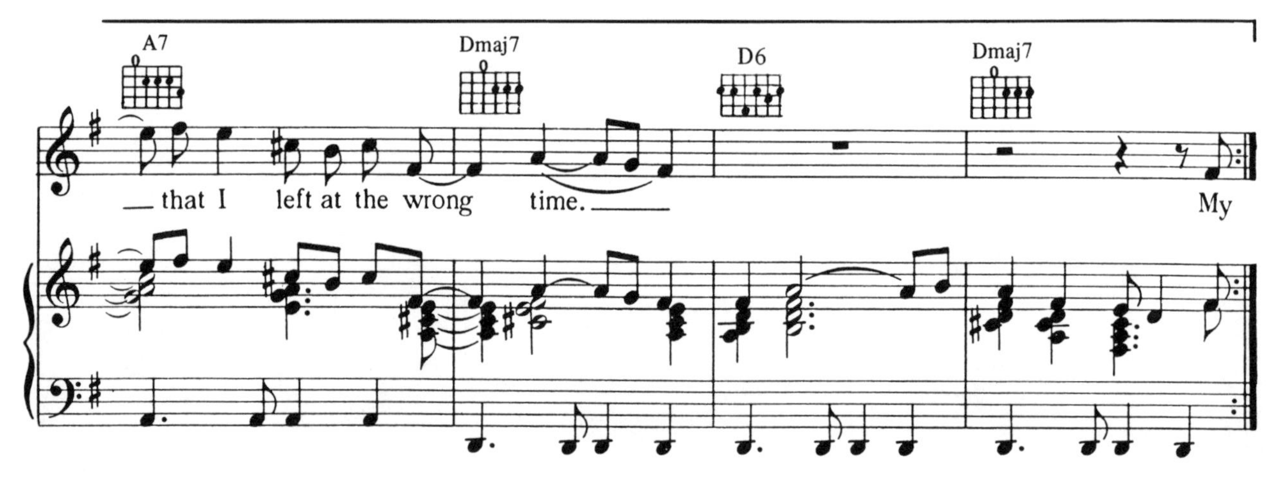
A7
Dmaj7
D6
Dmaj7
that I left at the wrong time.
My

2.
A6
Fmaj7
Bb6
Fmaj7
I soon found out that my lone-ly life was-n't so pret - ty

Bb6
Bbmaj7
Bb7
I'm glad I went, Now I'm that much more sure that we're rea-

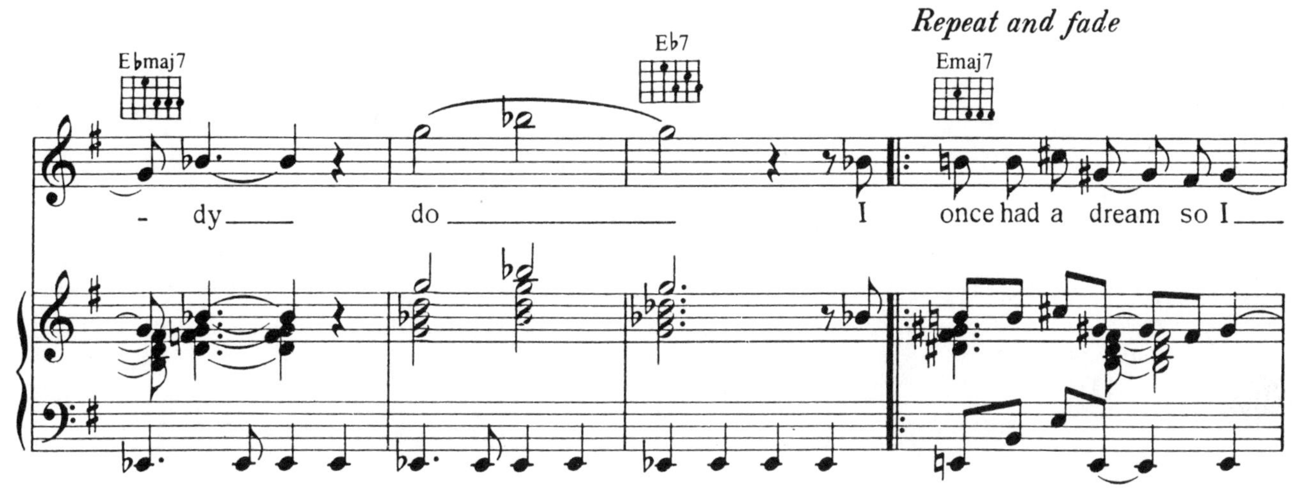
Repeat and fade
Ebmaj7
Eb7
Emaj7
-dy do I once had a dream so I

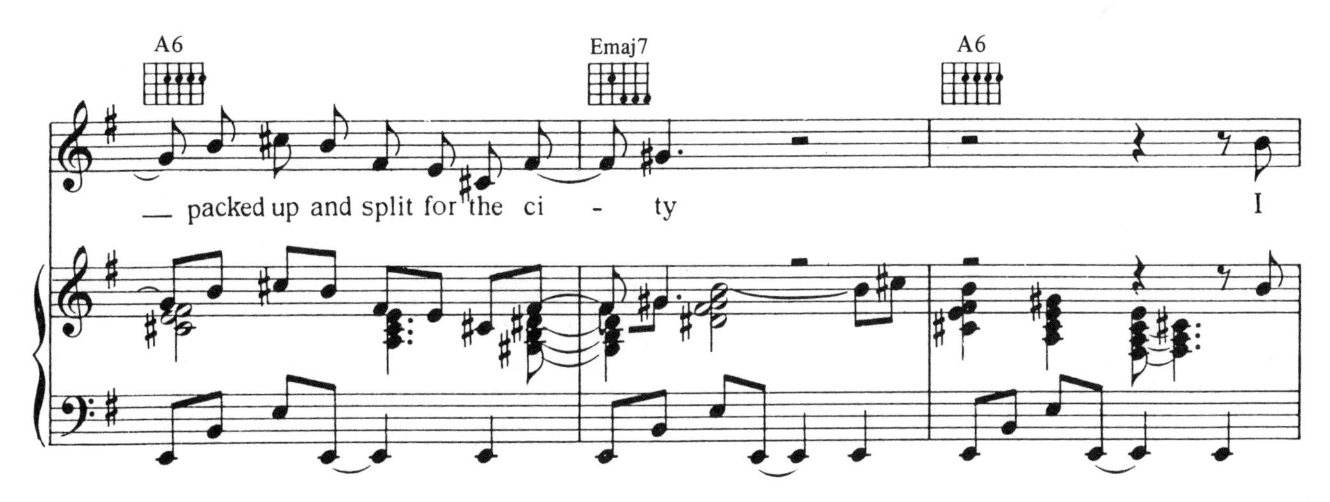
A6
Emaj7
A6
packed up and split for the ci - ty I

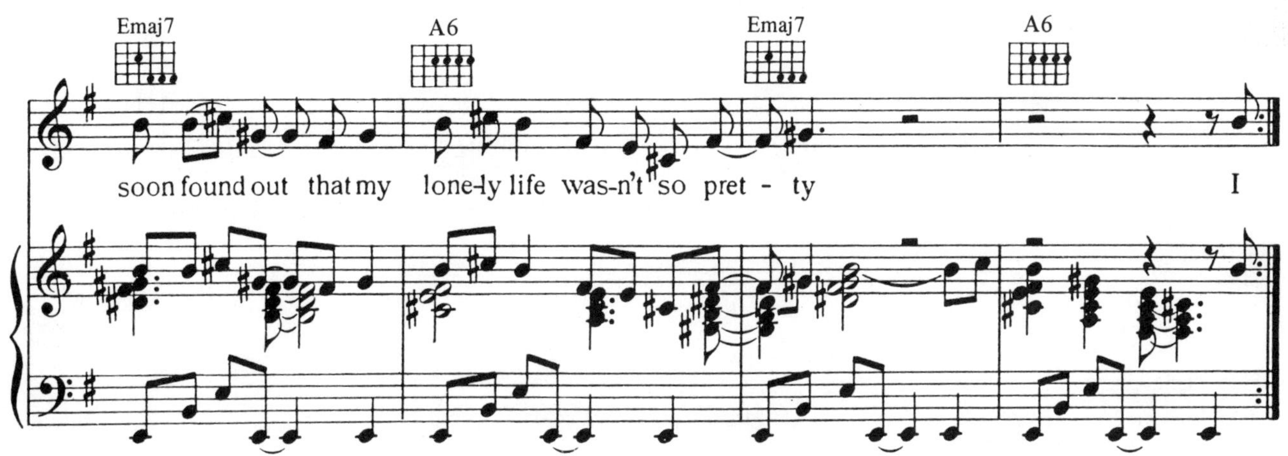
Emaj7
A6
Emaj7
A6
soon found out that my lone-ly life was-n't so pret - ty I

GIRLS ON THE BEACH

Words & Music by Brian Wilson

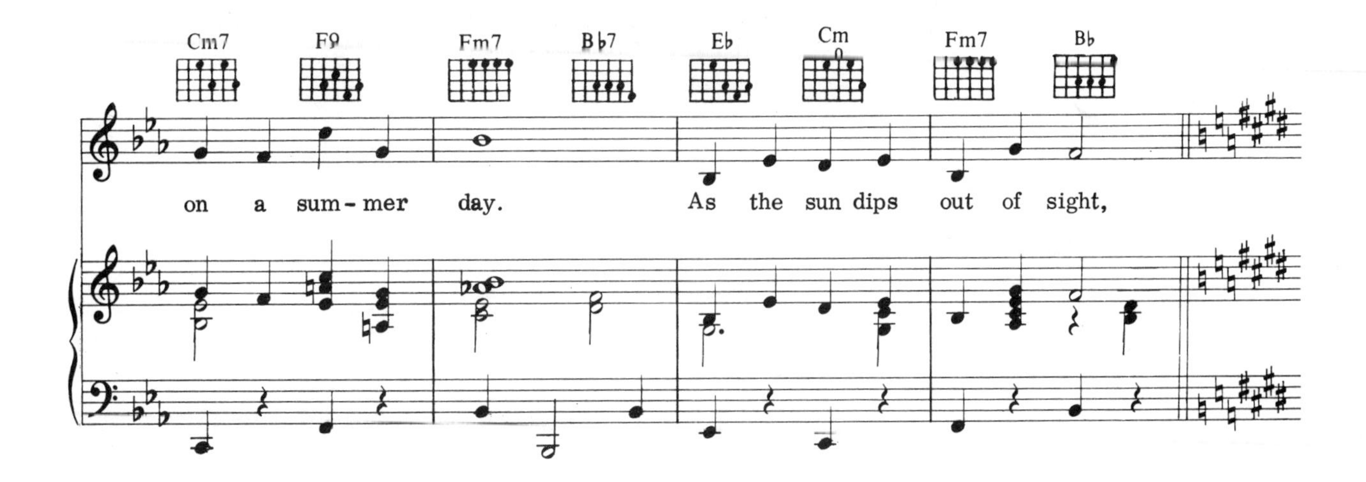
Cm7 F9 Fm7 B♭7 E♭ Cm Fm7 B♭
on a sum-mer day. As the sun dips out of sight,

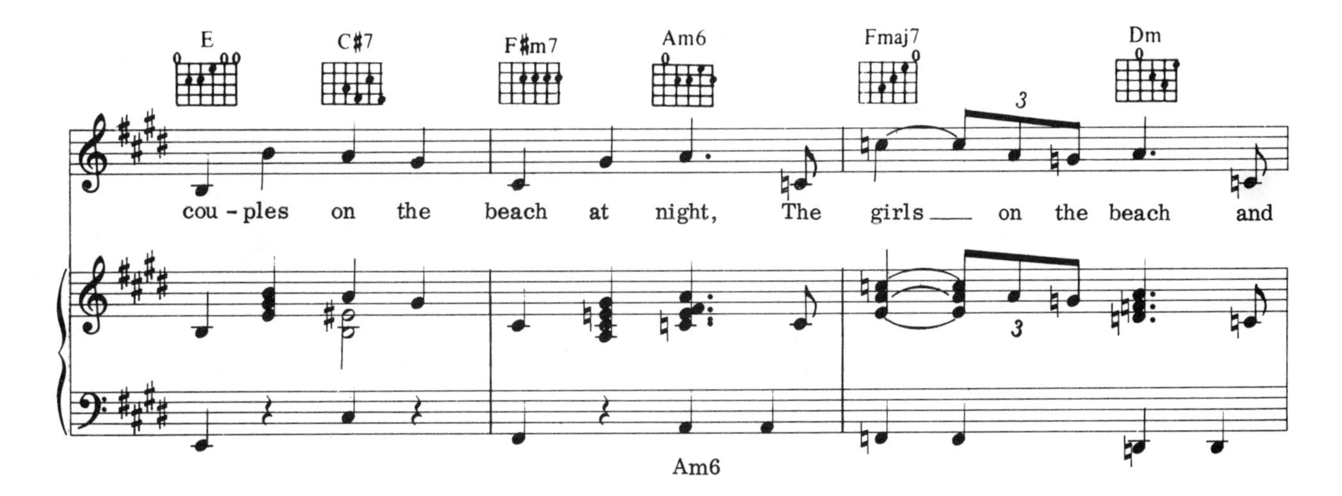
E C♯7 F♯m7 Am6 Fmaj7 Dm
cou-ples on the beach at night, The girls on the beach and
Am6

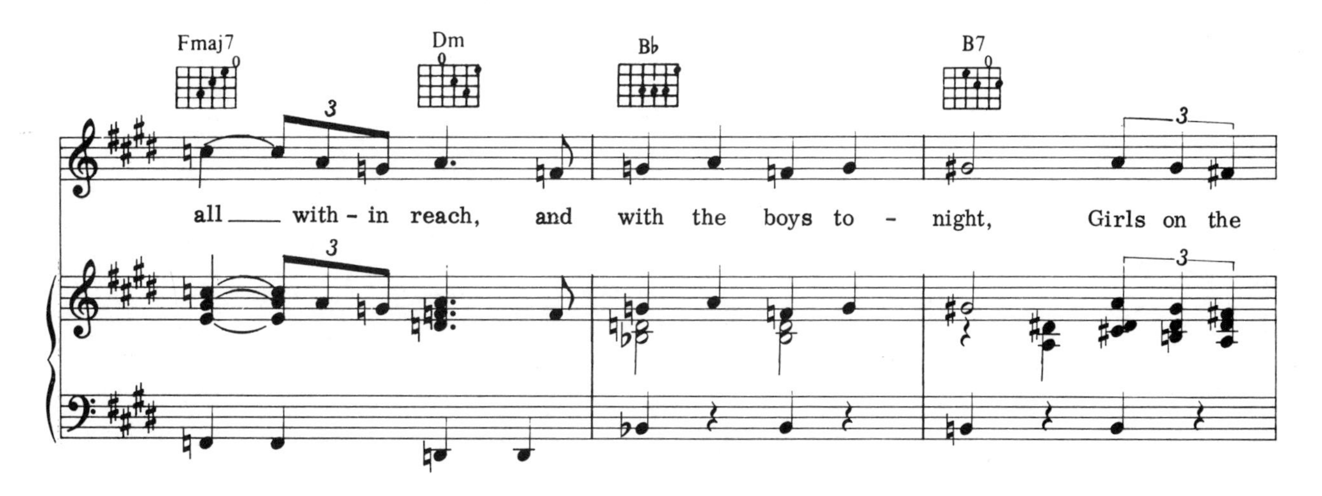
Fmaj7 Dm B♭ B7
all with-in reach, and with the boys to-night, Girls on the

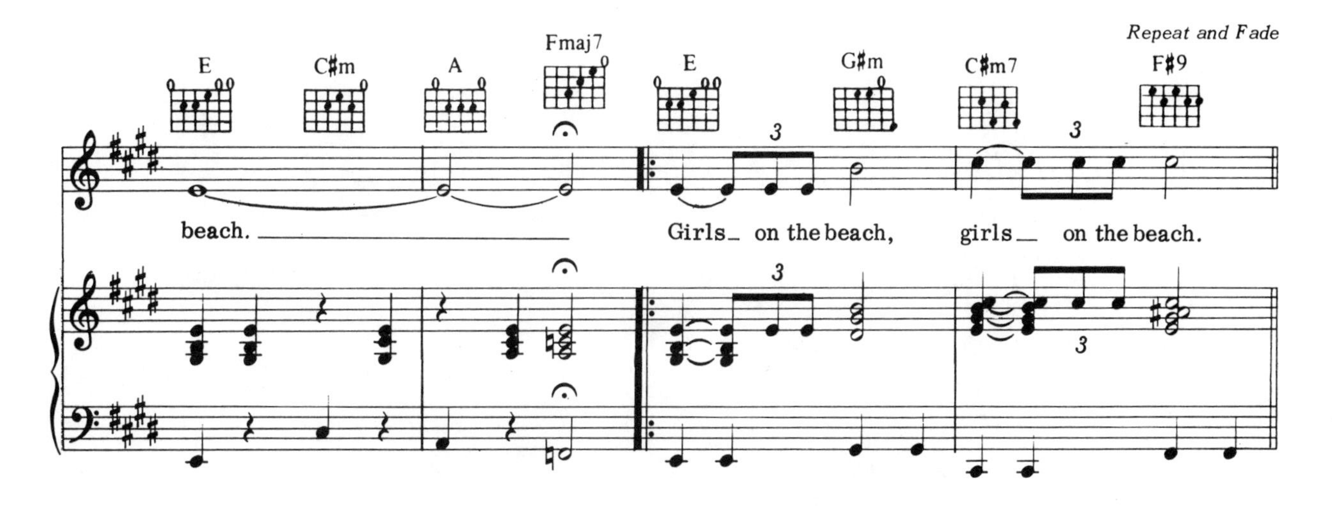
Repeat and Fade
E C♯m A Fmaj7 E G♯m C♯m7 F♯9
beach. Girls on the beach, girls on the beach.

LITTLE DEUCE COUPE

Words & Music by Brian Wilson & Roger Christian

C
F
purrs like a kit- ten till the lake pipes roar, _ And if that ain't e-nough to make you flip your wig, _ There's
D7
G7
C
one more thing, I've got the pink slip, Dad-dy! And com-in' off the line, when the lights turn green, _ She
F
blows 'em out-ta the wa-ter like you've nev-er seen. _ I get pushed out of shape, _ And it's hard to steer. _ When
C
G
Dm
G7
I get rub-ber in- a all four gears, She's my Lit-tle Deuce Coupe, You don't know _ what I've got! _
1. C
C7
2. C
C11
She's got a

SURF'S UP

Words & Music by Brian Wilson & Van Dyke Parks

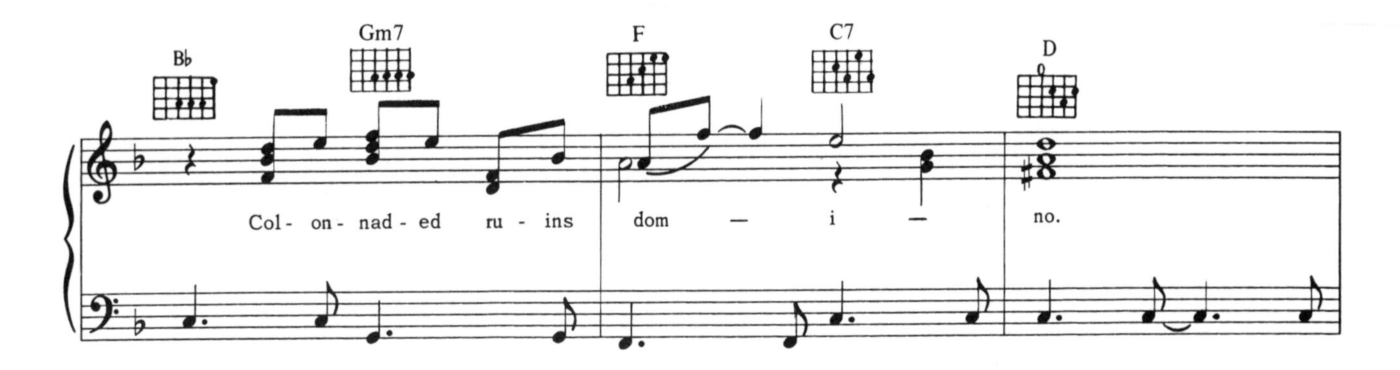
Bb
Gm7
F
C7
D
Col- on- nad- ed ru - ins dom — i — no.

1.
G
A
D
Can - vas the town and brush the back-drop. Are you sleep - ing?

2.
G
A
Can - vas the town and brush the back drop. Are you

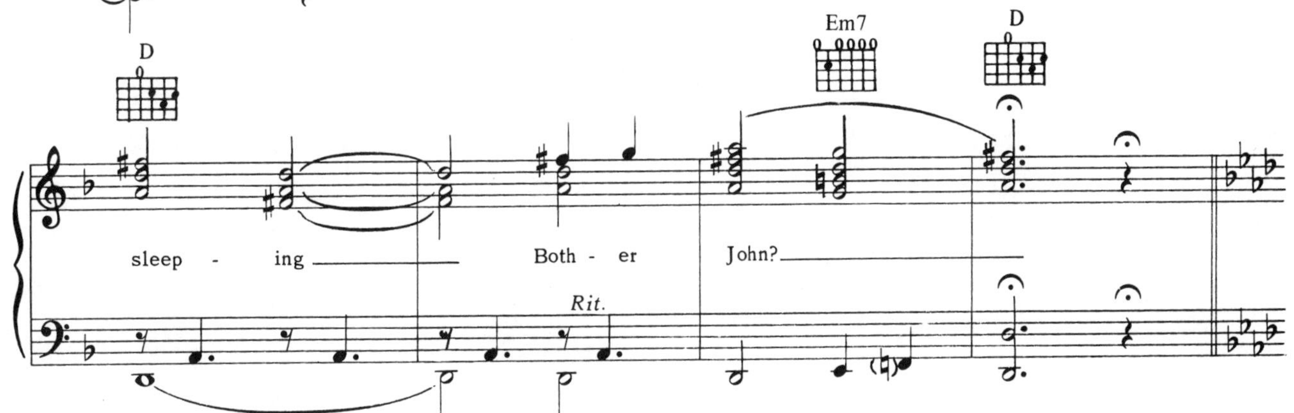
D
Em7
D
sleep - ing Both - er John?
Rit.

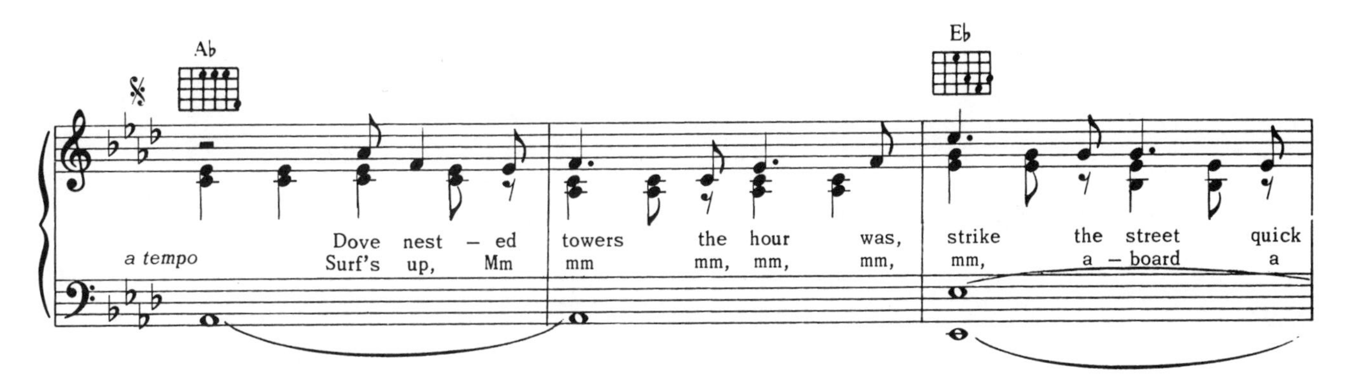
Ab
Eb
Dove nest - ed towers the hour was, strike the street quick
Surf's up, Mm mm mm, mm, mm, mm, a - board a
a tempo

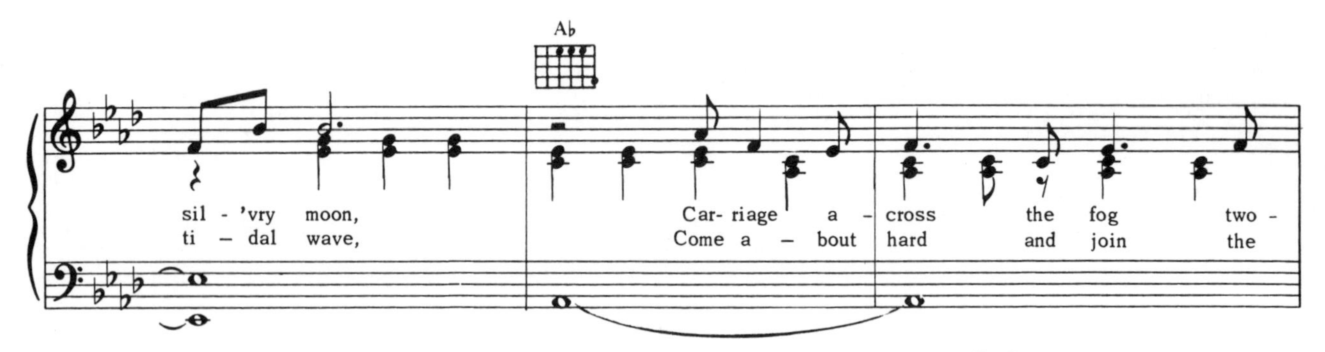
Ab
sil - 'vry moon, Car- riage a - cross the fog two -
ti - dal wave, Come a - bout hard and join the

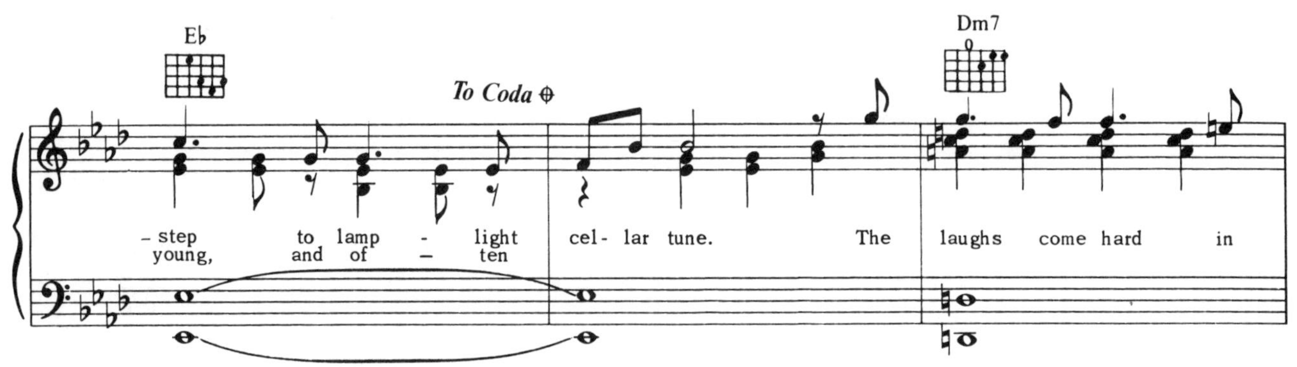
Eb
To Coda ⊕
Dm7
- step to lamp - light cel- lar tune. The laughs come hard in
young, and of - ten

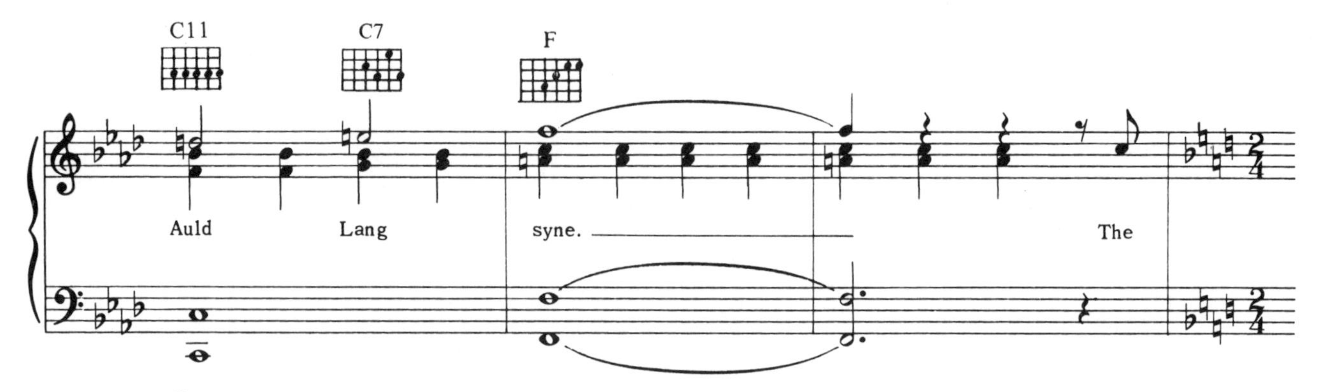
C11
C7
F
Auld Lang syne. The

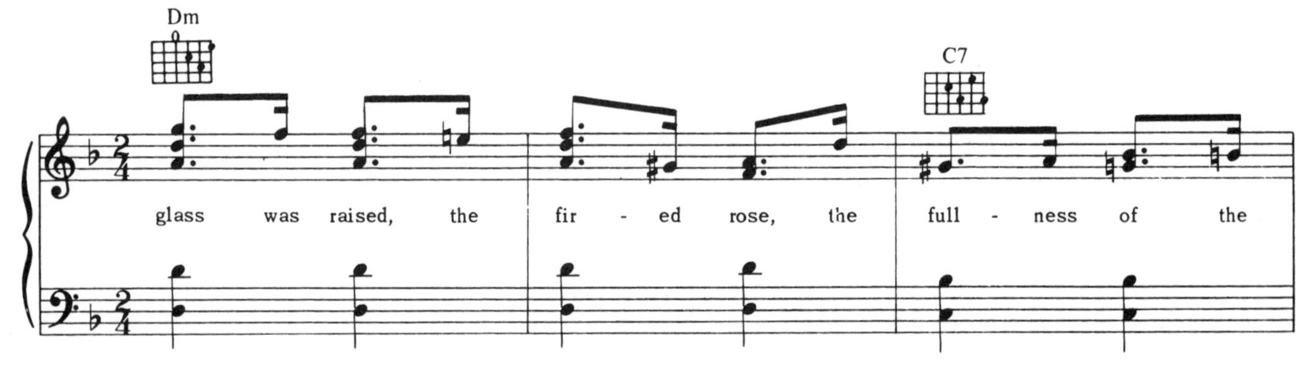
Dm
C7
glass was raised, the fir - ed rose, the full - ness of the

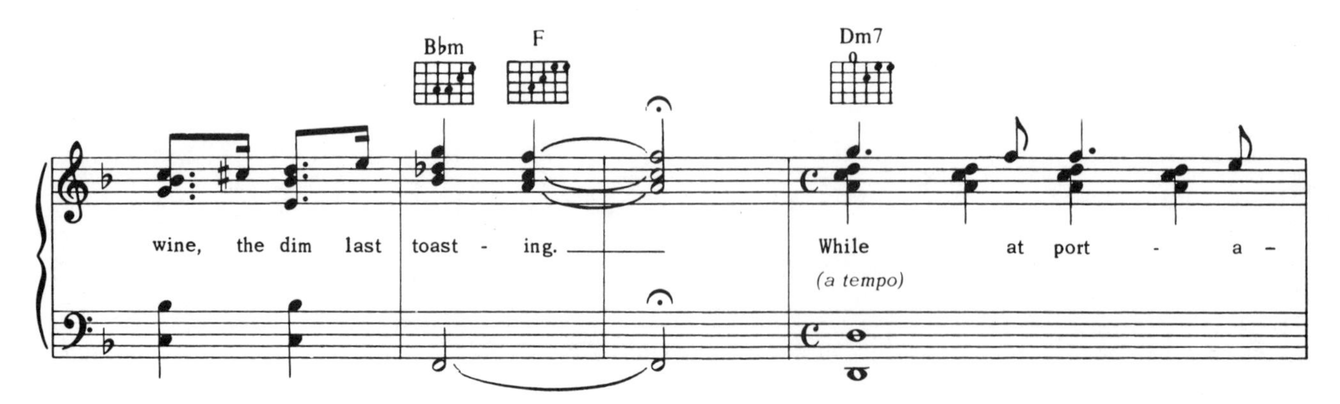
Bbm
F
Dm7
wine, the dim last toast - ing. While at port - a -
(a tempo)

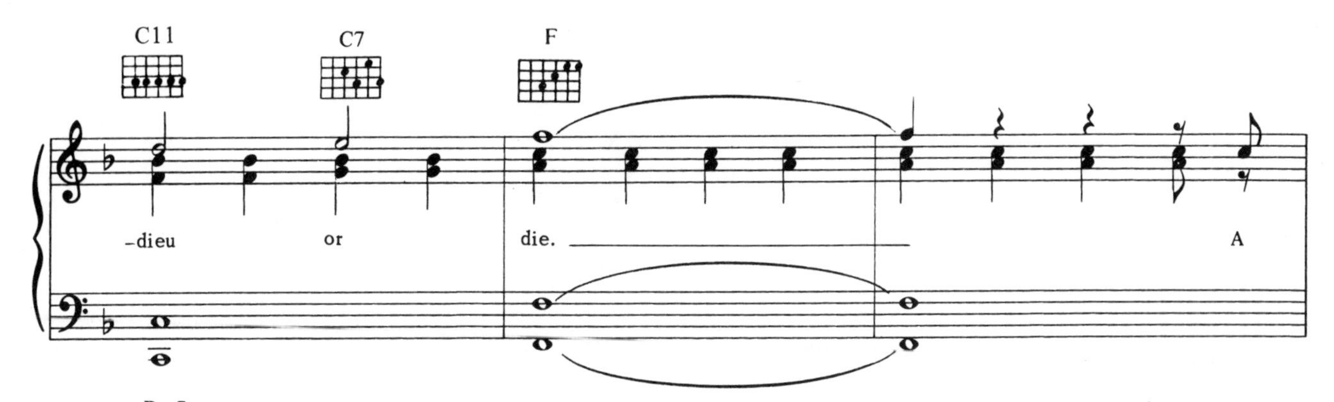
C11
C7
F
-dieu or die. A

Dm7
C7
choke of grief heart hard – ened I be - yond be - lief, a

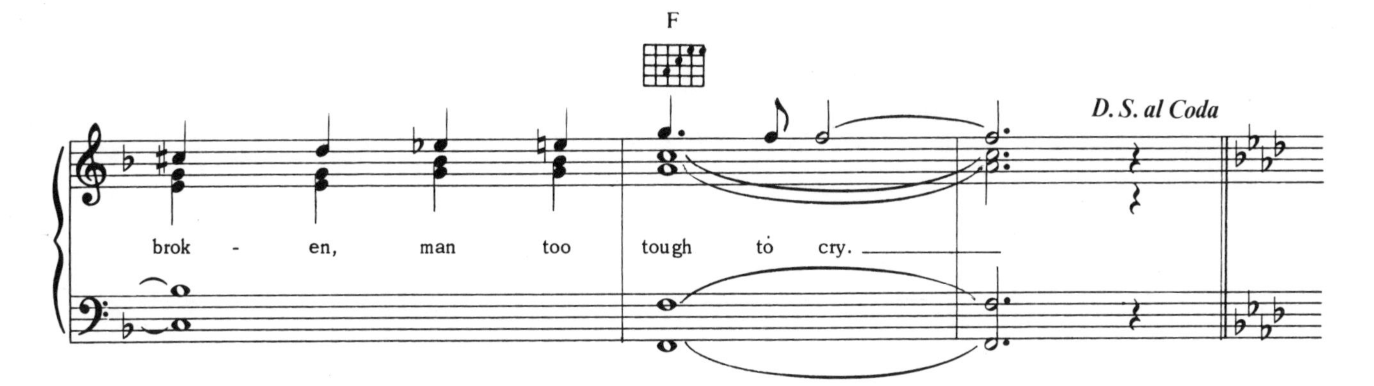
F
D. S. al Coda
brok - en, man too tough to cry.

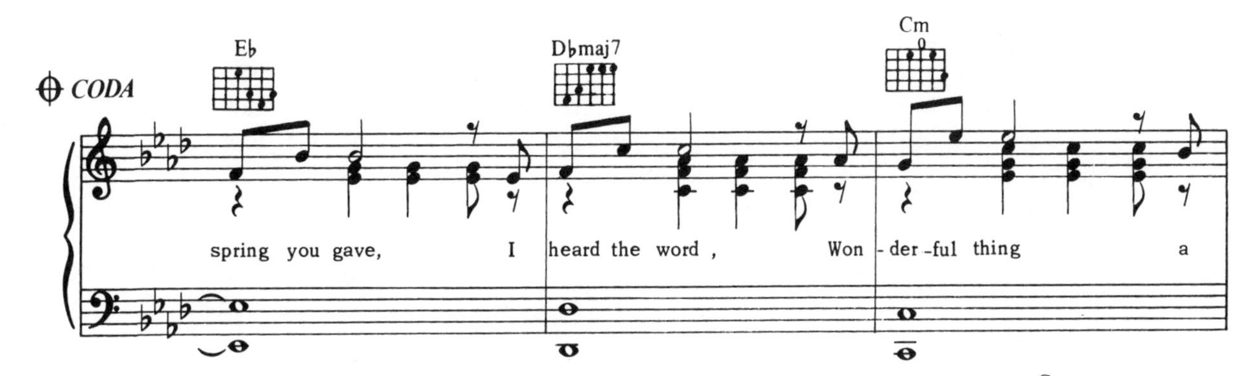
CODA
E♭
D♭maj7
Cm
spring you gave, I heard the word, Won - der - ful thing a

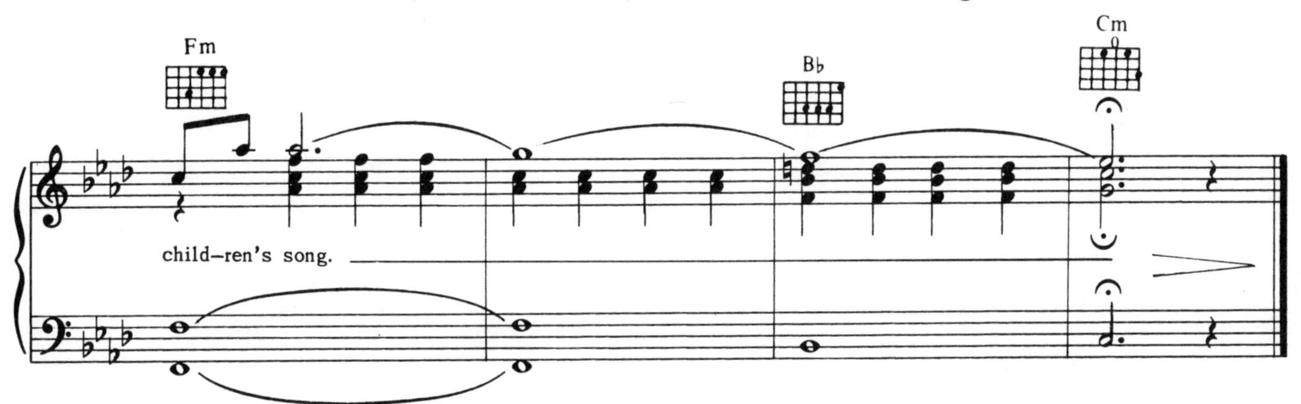
Fm
B♭
Cm
child–ren's song.

LET'S GO AWAY FOR A WHILE

Music by Brian Wilson & Tony Asher

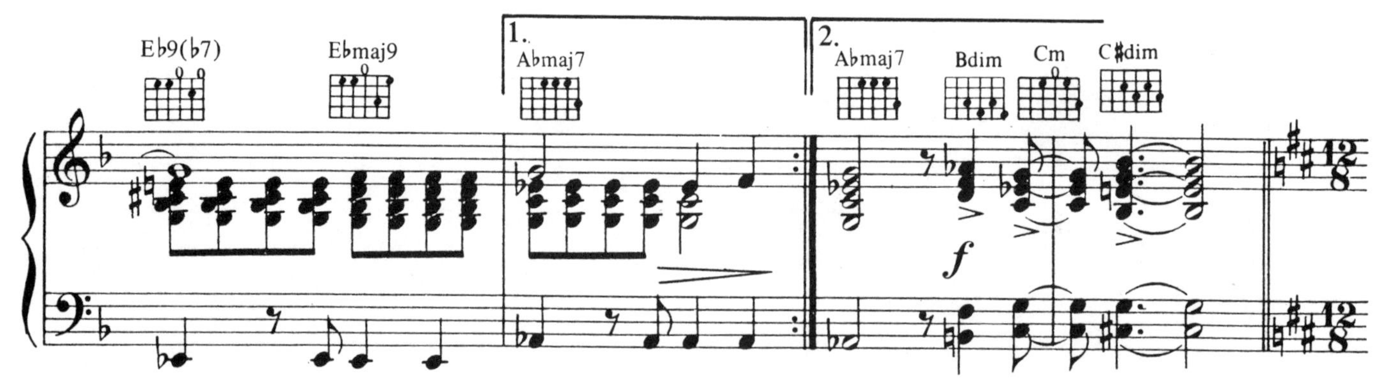

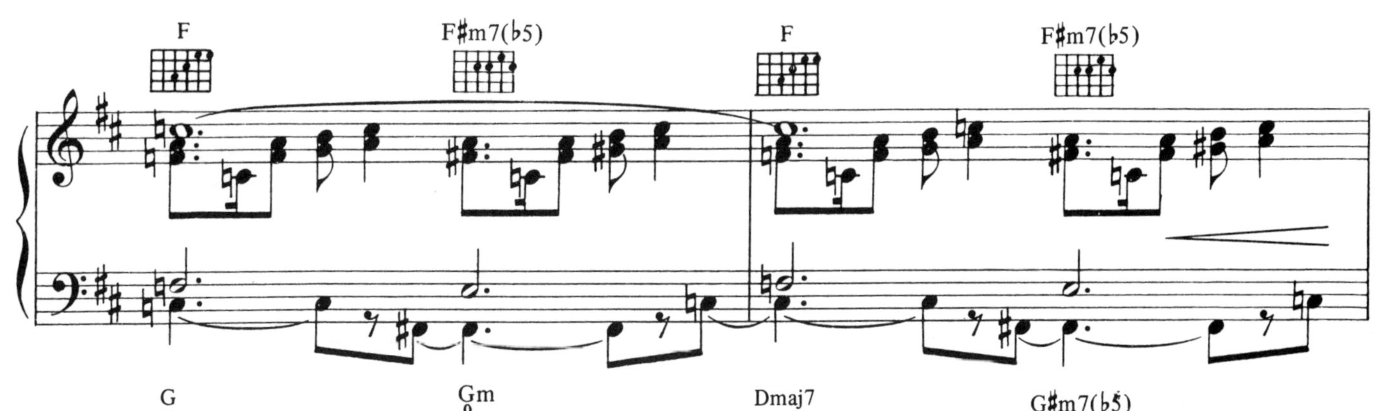
F
F♯m7(♭5)
F
F♯m7(♭5)

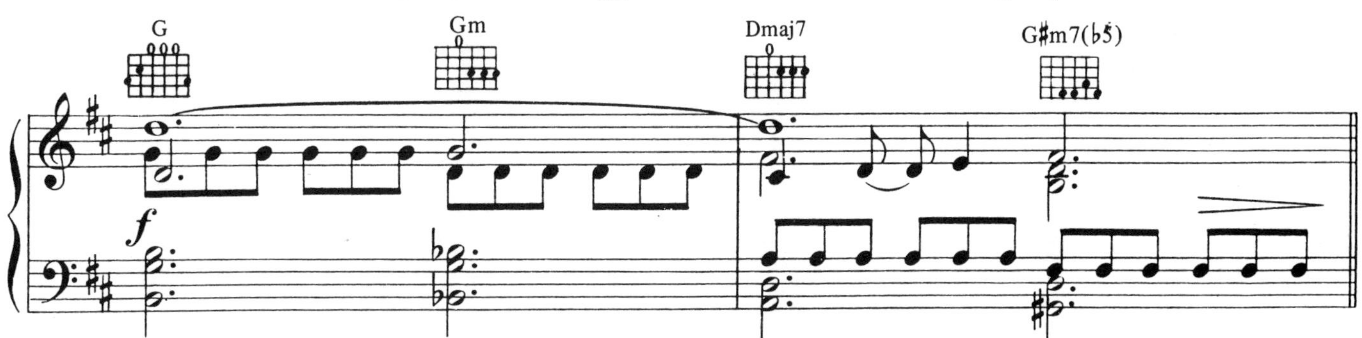
G
Gm
Dmaj7
G♯m7(♭5)
f

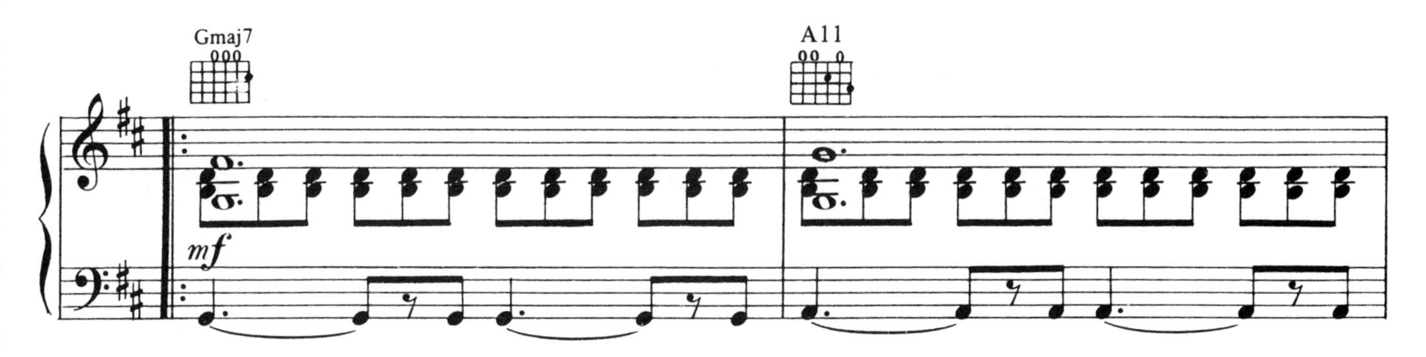
Gmaj7
A11
mf

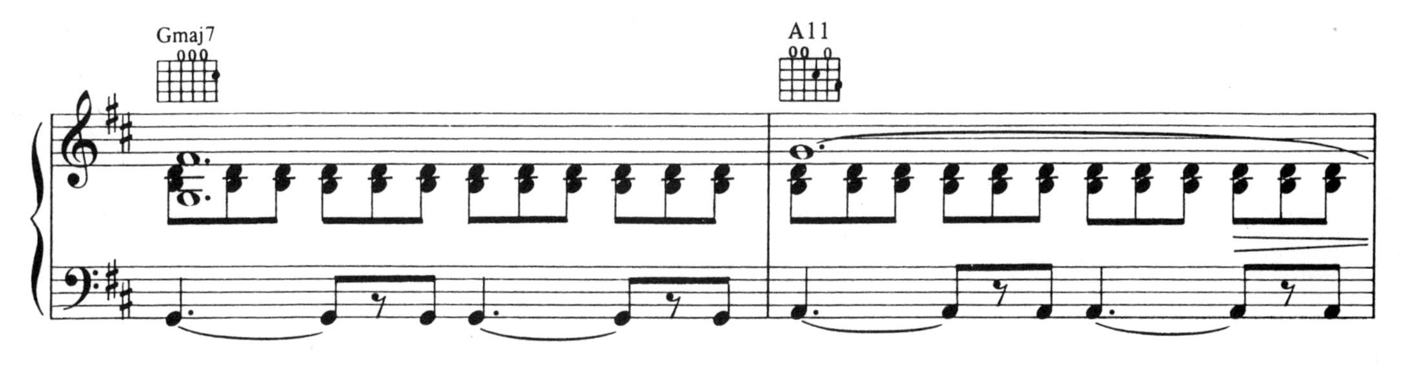
Gmaj7
A11

1.
A9
mp
2.
A9
mp
Dmaj7

WENDY

Words & Music by Brian Wilson

Cm
Eb
Ab
guy could cry, Till you made it with an - other guy, Oh,
you with him, His future looks awful dim, Oh,
from my mind, Was the day that I'd wake up to find My

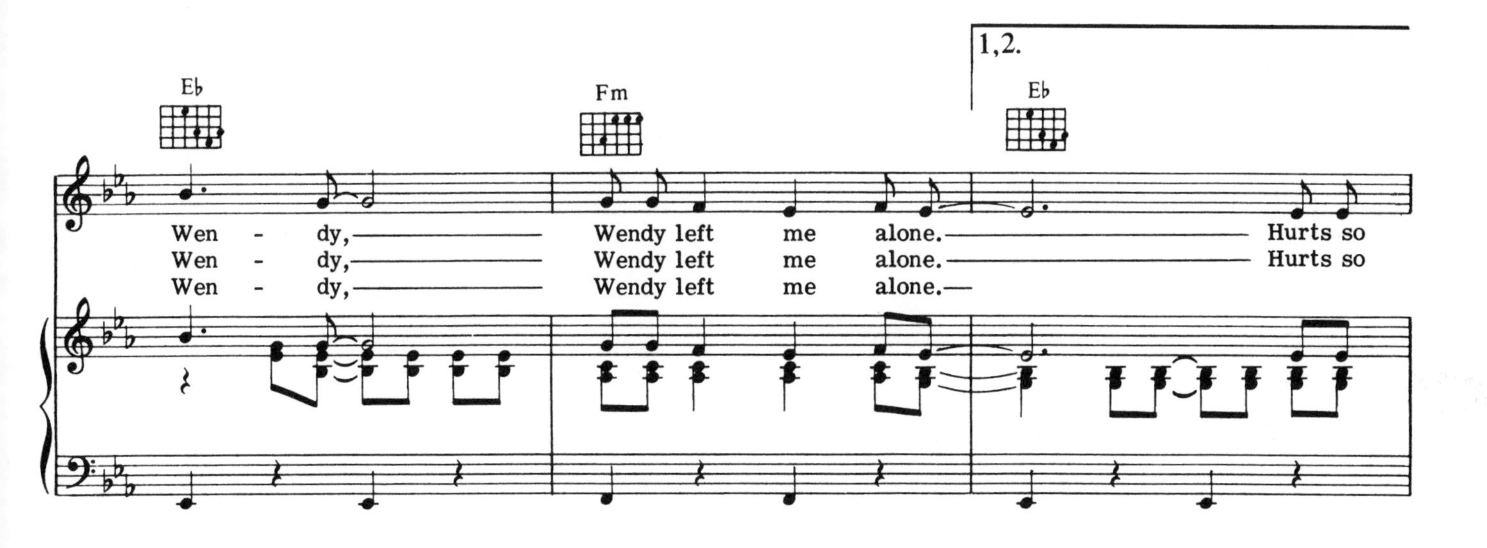
1,2.
Eb
Fm
Eb
Wen - dy, Wendy left me alone. Hurts so
Wen - dy, Wendy left me alone. Hurts so
Wen - dy, Wendy left me alone.

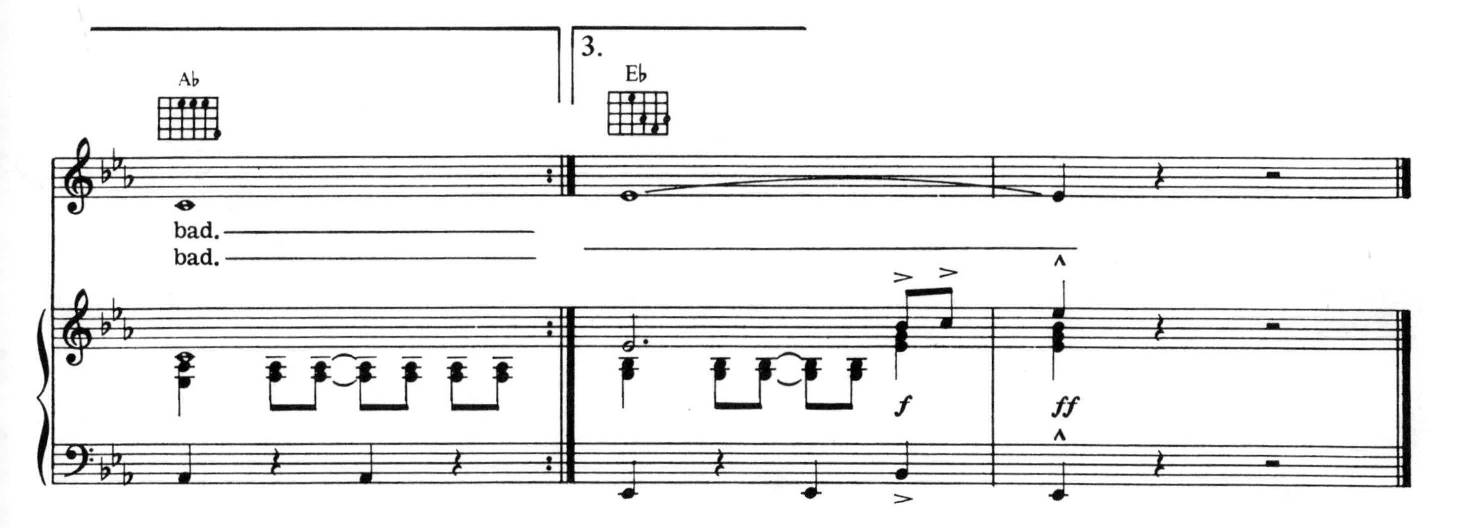
3.
Ab
Eb
bad.
bad.
f
ff

SIDEWALK SURFIN'

Words & Music by Brian Wilson & Roger Christian

D
Qua - si - mo - to or the Cof - fin too Why don't you
Shake a - ya bun - ga now and skate right on thru Why don't you
side - walks cracked you bet - ter pull out quick. Why don't you
1,2.
A7
Em7
A7
D
grab your board and go Side - walk Surf - in' with me.
3.
A7
Em7
A7
D
grab your board and go Side - walk Surf - in' with me.
Come on and
A7
Em7
A7
D
grab your board and go Side - walk Surf - in' with me.

SALT LAKE CITY

Words & Music by Brian Wilson

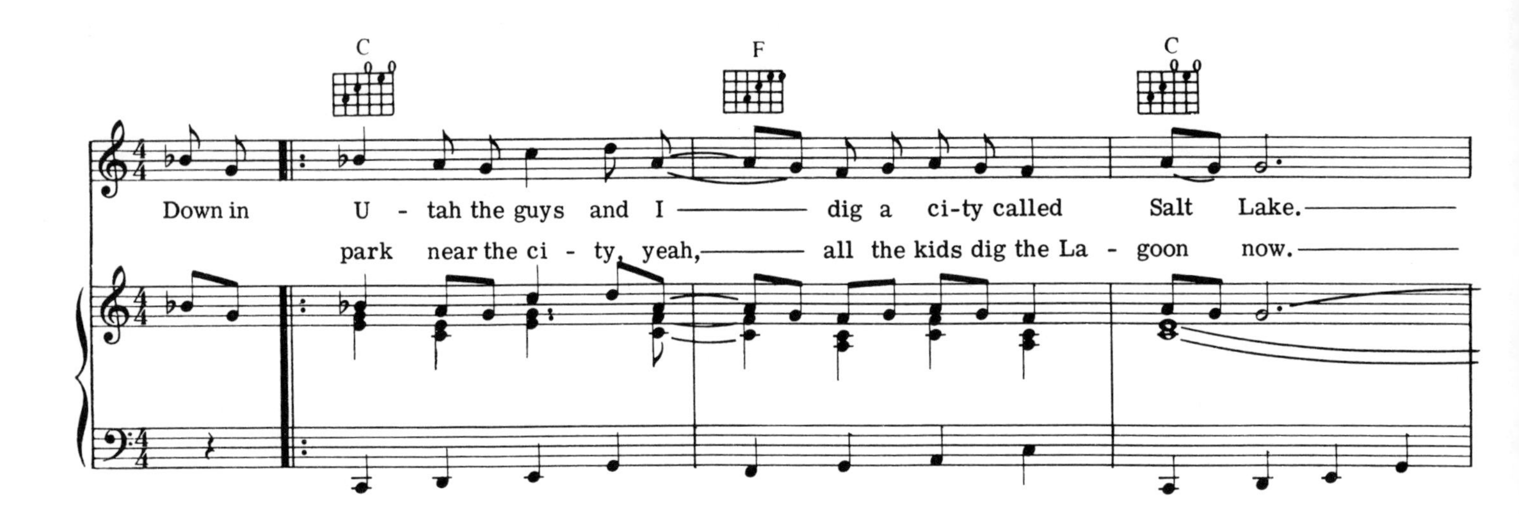

Dm7
Gm7
C
is an out of sight thing.
And the
test of the Wes - tern states.
They got the
F
G
Number One ra-di—o sta tion makes the town really swing.
sun in the summer and win ter time the ski-ing is great.
Dm7
G9
G7
G9
G7
Salt Lake Ci - ty, we'll be co - min'
1.
C
2.
C
soon.
There's a
soon.

IN MY ROOM

Words & Music by Brian Wilson & Gary Usher

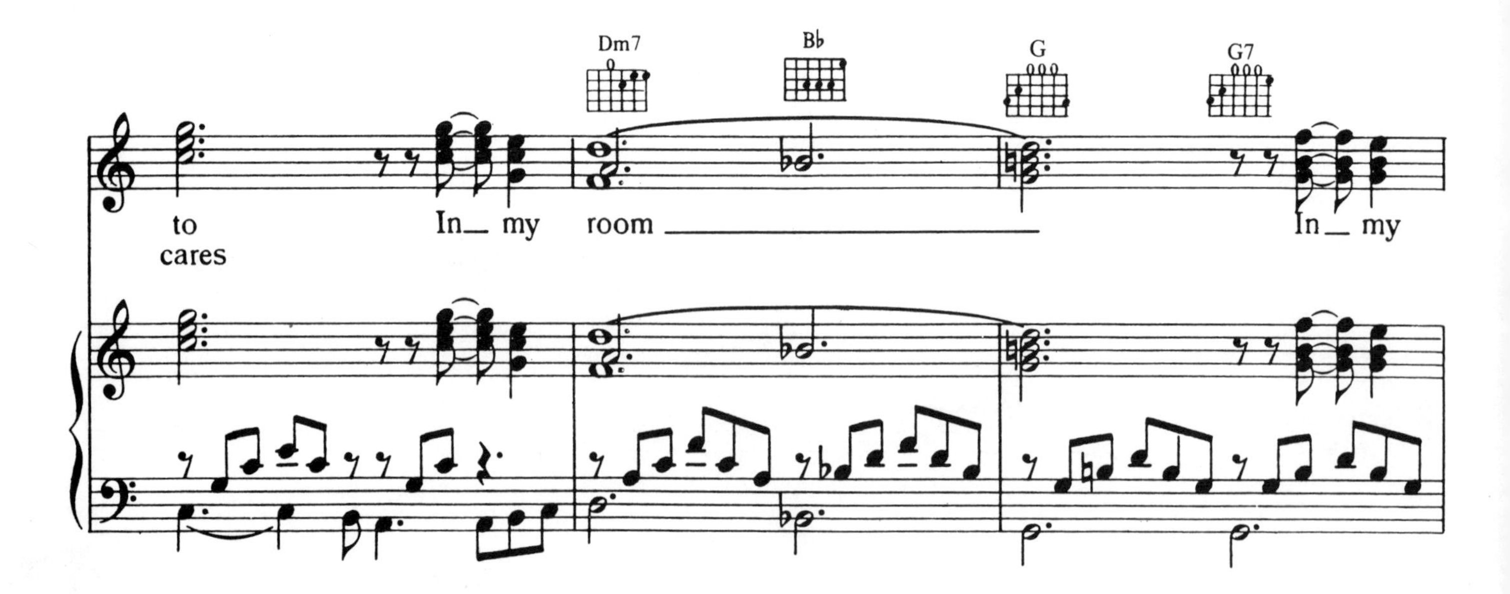

1.
C
Db
C
2.
C
Bb
room.
In my room.
room.
In my

C
Am
G
Do my dream - ing And my schem - ing
room.

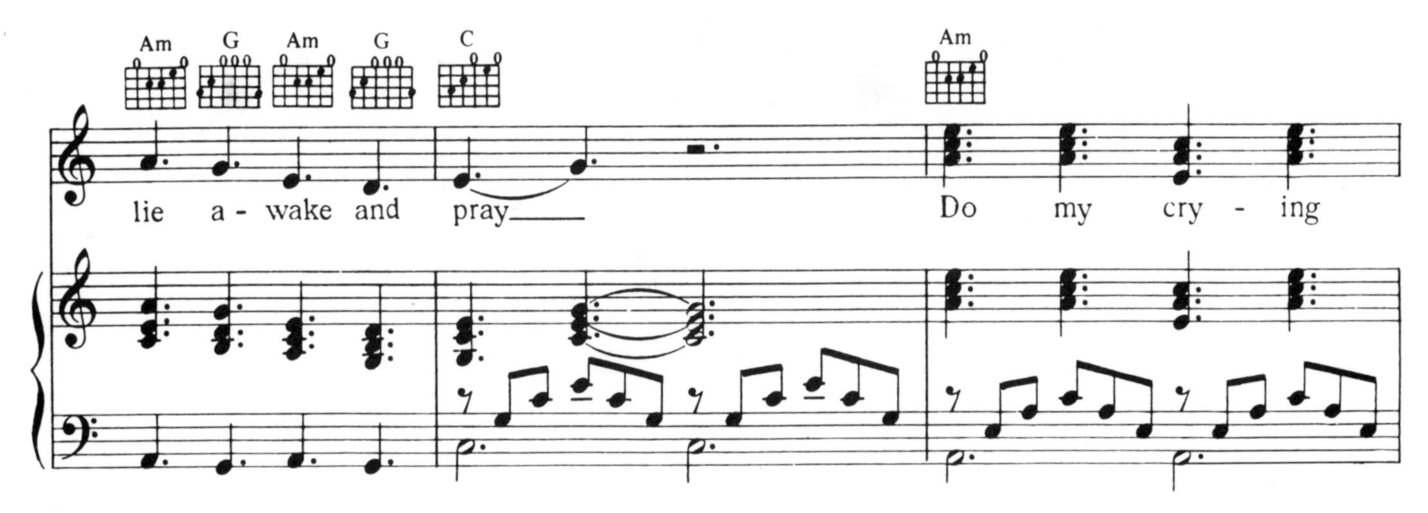
Am
G
Am
G
C
Am
lie a - wake and pray
Do my cry - ing

G
Dm7
G7
And my sigh - ing Laugh at yes - ter - day

C
Bb
Now it's dark and I'm a - lone but I won't be a -
Dm7
Bb
G
- fraid In my room In my
C
Bb
C
Bb
C
Bb
room.
room.
room In my room In my room In my
C
Bb
C
Bb
C
room In my room In my room.

SUMMERTIME BLUES

Words & Music by Eddie Cochran & Jerry Capehart

F
G7
C
G
Some-times I won-der what I'm a-gon-na do, But there ain't no cure for the Sum-mer-time Blues.
2. A well my
3. (I'm gon-na)
Mom 'n' Pa-pa told me, "Son, you got-ta make some mo-ney, If you
take two weeks Gon-na have a fine va-ca-tion, I'm gon-na
want-ta use the car to go a-rid-in' next Sun-day," Well, I
take my prob-lem to the U-ni-ted Na-tions! Well, I

tacet
Spoken
F
did - n't go to work Told the boss I was sick "Now you can't use the car 'cause you
called my Con-gress-man and he said (quote) "I'd like to help you, Son, but you're
did - n't work a lick."
too young to vote."
F
G7
Some-times I won-der what I'm a-gon-na do, But there
C
G7
C
ain't no cure for the Sum-mer-time Blues.
1
F
G
C
3. I'm gon-na
2
F
G
C
F
G
C

I GET AROUND

Words & Music by Brian Wilson

C
B♭
G7
VERSE
I'm mak-in' real good bread.
1. I'm get-tin'
2. We
Dm7
(tacet)
bugged, driv-in' up an' down the same ol' strip I got-ta find a new place where the
al-ways take my car 'cause it's nev-er been beat and we've nev-er missed yet with the
kids are hip
girls we meet
My
None of the
bud-dies and me are get-tin' real well known, Yeah, the bad guys know us and they
guys go stea-dy 'cause it would-n't be right to leave your best girl home on a

G7
(tacet)
CHORUS
C
leave us a - lone. — I get a - round from town to
Sat - ur - day night. —
A7
Dm
A
Dm
town
I'm a real cool head
C
B♭
1. G7
— I'm mak- in' real good bread.
2. We
2. G7
C
Am
Repeat till fade-out
(Spoken) I get around, etc.